Scott, Foresman Encore Readers

STRIKE UP THE BAND

Authors

Ira E. Aaron
Rena Koke

Books

Clap Your Hands
In the Spotlight
Hurrah! Hurrah!
On with the Show
Giggles and Grins
Strike Up the Band
Take a Bow

Scott, Foresman and Company
Editorial Offices: Glenview, Illinois

Regional Sales Offices: Palo Alto, California •
Tucker, Georgia • Glenview, Illinois •
Oakland, New Jersey • Dallas, Texas

Acknowledgment

page 66 top: H. Armstrong Roberts

Contents

Section One

ISBN 0-673-11395-7

Copyright © 1980,
Scott, Foresman and Company, Glenview, Illinois.
All Rights Reserved.
Printed in the United States of America.

12345678910-KPK-8887868584838281 8079

2

Section Two

Section One

The String Collection

by Mary Radloff

Mr. Fergus was a collector. He collected bottles with pretty shapes, boxes of all sizes, rocks of many colors, and seashells from the beaches of the world.

One day as Mr. Fergus was walking down Main Street, he found a piece of red string. Mr. Fergus stooped down and picked it up.

"This," said Mr. Fergus to himself, "is the beginning of my string collection!" He wound the piece of red string into a ball and put it in his pocket.

Mr. Fergus stopped at the market for a pound of meat for supper. He was pleased to see the butcher tie the package with a piece of white string.

When Mr. Fergus got home, he removed the white string from the package, tied one end to the end of his ball of red string, and wound it carefully around. The ball of string was now a little larger.

Mr. Fergus put the ball in a special drawer and marked it with the words *String Collection*.

Every day Mr. Fergus added to his string collection. He bought new shoes, and the clerk tied the box with soft brown string. Mr. Fergus tied the brown string to the end of his collection and wound it around. The ball grew larger.

Mr. Fergus bought three shirts at the big department store and carried them home by the strong green string around the package. He tied the end of the green string to his collection and wound it around. The ball grew larger.

One day the letter carrier delivered a book. The package was tied with fuzzy black string. Mr. Fergus tied the black string to his collection and wound it around. The ball grew larger.

Soon Mr. Fergus's string collection was so large it would no longer fit in the drawer. He moved it to a shelf in the kitchen. One night the huge ball rolled right off the shelf. Mr. Fergus just barely managed to roll the large ball of string through the kitchen door and out into the backyard.

Soon the children of the town learned of Mr. Fergus's string collection. They began to bring him string from lunch bags, string from old pull toys, and string they found in drawers at home.

The string collection grew so large that Mr. Fergus had to use his ladder to reach the top of the ball to tie and wind more string. He was so busy tying and winding he had no time at all for collecting bottles, boxes, rocks, or seashells from the beaches of the world.

9

Now the ball of string was so large it filled his entire backyard. He had no room for flowers, no room for grass. The ball of string was so large it shaded his kitchen window and the room was dark and gloomy.

"This is enough!" cried Mr. Fergus at the end of one long day spent in tying and winding string. "I am through collecting string. I am through tying and winding. I want my yard back with green grass and flowers."

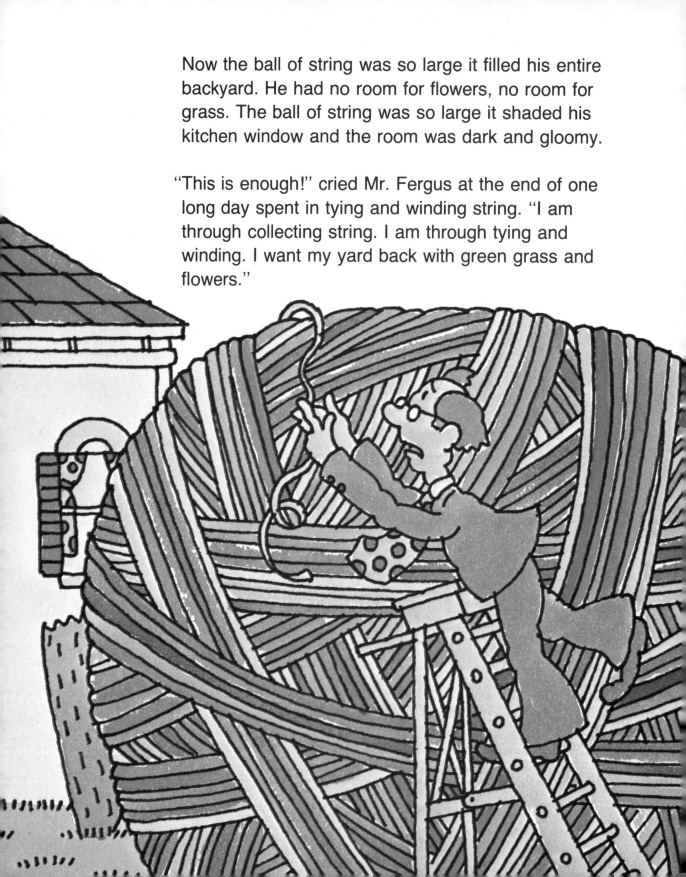

Mr. Fergus felt much better after that, but he still had one problem. He still had a yard filled with a ball of string. It was too big to carry; it was too heavy to lift; it was too large to roll. How would he ever get rid of such a large collection of string?

Mr. Fergus thought and thought, and at last he had an idea! He went into his house and was very busy with paper, sticks, rags, and even a bit of string. He hummed as he worked, and when he went to bed that night, he was a happy man.

The next day was bright and sunny. Mr. Fergus did nothing.

The second day was cool and rainy. Mr. Fergus did nothing.

The third day was brisk and windy. Mr. Fergus went out carrying the paper-stick-rag-string-thing he had made. He tied one end of it to the end of his string collection. It looked a little like—very much like—like it was a kite!

Mr. Fergus waited for a good gust of wind and tossed the kite into the air. As the kite went up, it took with it Mr. Fergus's string collection. As the kite went higher, the ball of string grew smaller. All morning, all afternoon, on into the early evening the ball of string disappeared as the kite disappeared.

At last both the kite and the collection were gone forever.

Just then the wind tossed a little feather at the feet of Mr. Fergus.

"Hmmm," said Mr. Fergus as he stooped to pick it up. "This is the beginning of my new collection."

What Do You Think?

1. How did Mr. Fergus get the idea for collecting string?
2. How did Mr. Fergus feel at the beginning of the story about his string collection?
3. Why did Mr. Fergus decide he no longer wanted to collect string?
4. Do you think Mr. Fergus will grow tired of his feather collection? Why or why not?
5. What is the meaning of *wound* in this sentence? She wound her arms around her dog.
   a. hurt or injure
   b. fold, wrap, or place about something

Activities

1. Make a list of all the things you would like to collect.
2. Make up a story about Mr. Fergus and his feather collection.

HA! HA!

compiled by E. Richard Churchill

What animal is the best baseball player?
   The bat.

When is it proper to go to bed with your shoes on?
   When you are a horse.

Why do elephants have trunks?
   They would look silly with glove compartments.

What insect is a good baseball player?
   The spider. It catches flies.

What fruit is on coins?
   The date.

The Elephant's Picnic

by Richard Hughes

Elephants are generally clever animals, but
there was once an elephant who was very silly.
His best friend was a kangaroo. Now kangaroos
are not often clever animals, and this one
certainly was not. So the kangaroo and the
elephant got along very well together.

One day the elephant and the kangaroo
thought they would like to go off for a picnic by
themselves. But they did not know anything
about picnics and had not the faintest idea of
what to do to get ready.

"The Elephant's Picnic" from *The Wonder Dog & To* by Richard Hughes,
published by Chatto & Windus. Reprinted by permission of David Higham
Associates, Limited.

"What do you do on a picnic?" the elephant asked a child he knew.

"Oh, we collect wood and make a fire, and then we boil the kettle," said the child.

"What do you boil the kettle for?" asked the elephant in surprise.

"Why, for tea, of course," said the child in a snapping sort of way.

So the elephant did not ask any more questions but went and told the kangaroo. Then they collected together all the things they thought they would need.

16

When they got to their picnic place, the kangaroo said that she would collect the wood because she had a pouch to carry it back in. A kangaroo's pouch, of course, is very small. So the kangaroo carefully chose the smallest twigs she could find. She chose only about five or six. In fact, it took a lot of hopping to find any sticks small enough to go in her pouch at all. It was a long time before she came back. But silly though the elephant was, he soon saw those sticks would not be enough for a fire.

"Now I will go off and get some wood," he said.

17

The elephant's ideas of getting wood were very different. He did not take little twigs. Instead he pushed down whole trees with his forehead. He staggered back to the picnic place with the trees rolled up in his trunk.

The kangaroo struck a match and lit a bonfire made of whole trees. The blaze was enormous, and the fire was so hot that for a long time they could not get near it. It was not until it began to die down a bit that they were able to get near enough to cook anything.

"Now let's boil the kettle," said the elephant. Among the things he had brought were a brightly shining copper kettle and a very large black iron saucepan. The elephant filled the saucepan with water.

"What are you doing that for?" asked the kangaroo.

"To boil the kettle in, you silly," said the elephant. So he popped the kettle in the saucepan of water and put the saucepan on the fire. He did this because he thought that a kettle is boiled in the same way an egg or a cabbage is boiled. The kangaroo did not know any better either.

So they boiled and boiled the kettle and every now and then they prodded it with a stick.

"It doesn't seem to be getting tender," said the elephant sadly. "I'm sure we can't eat it for tea until it does."

So then away he went and got more wood for the fire. And still the saucepan boiled and boiled, and still the kettle remained as hard as ever.

It was getting late now, almost dark. "I am afraid it won't be ready for tea," said the kangaroo. "I am afraid we shall have to spend the night here. I wish we had brought something with us to sleep in."

"Didn't you?" said the elephant. "You mean to say you didn't pack before you came?"

"No," said the kangaroo. "What should I have packed anyway?"

"Why, your trunk, of course," said the elephant. "That is what people pack."

"But I haven't got a trunk," said the kangaroo.

"Well, I have," said the elephant, "and I've packed it! Kindly pass the pepper. I want to unpack!"

So the kangaroo passed the elephant the pepper, and the elephant took a good sniff. Then he gave a most tremendous sneeze, and everything he had packed in his trunk shot out of it. Out came toothbrush, spare socks, gym shoes, a comb, a bag of marbles, his pajamas, and his Sunday suit. So then the elephant put on his pajamas and lay down to sleep.

But the kangaroo had no pajamas, and so, of course, she could not possibly sleep. "All right," she said to the elephant. "You sleep, and I will sit up and keep the fire going."

All night the kangaroo kept the fire blazing brightly and the kettle boiling merrily in the saucepan. When the next morning came, the elephant woke up.

"Now," he said, "let's have our breakfast."

21

They took the kettle out of the saucepan; and what do you think? *It was boiled as tender as tender as tender could be!* So they cut it fairly in half and shared it between them and ate it for breakfast. And they both agreed that they had never had such a good breakfast in their lives.

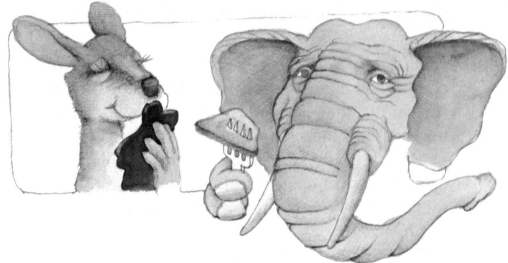

What Do You Think?

1. What did the child mean when she said "boil the kettle"? What did the elephant think "boil the kettle" meant?
2. Why did the kangaroo collect small sticks for the fire? Why was the elephant able to gather whole trees for the fire?
3. Where did the elephant pack his clothes?
4. Were you surprised at the ending of the story? Why or why not?

Activity

Draw a picture of the part of the story you liked best.

PANCAKE?

by Shel Silverstein

Who wants a pancake,
Sweet and piping hot?
Good little Grace looks up and says,
"I'll take the one on top."
Who else wants a pancake,
Fresh off the griddle?
Terrible Theresa smiles and says,
"I'll take the one in the middle."

A Clever Woman

by Hope Newell

The Little Old Woman had only one blanket, but it was full of holes. "I must get a new blanket before the winter comes," she said. "Or better yet, I might buy myself a feather bed. How warm and cozy I would be in a feather bed on cold winter nights!"

But feather beds cost a lot of money, so the Little Old Woman bought a flock of geese instead. As she was driving them home from the market, she said to herself, "These twelve geese will lay eggs for me all summer. Then when winter comes I will clip their feathers and make myself a feather bed. What a clever Old Woman I am!"

Adapted from *The Little Old Woman Who Used Her Head* by Hope Newell. Copyright © 1962 by Hope Newell. Reprinted by permission of the Publisher, Elsevier/Nelson Books.

When the Little Old Woman arrived home, she drove the geese into the yard and closed the gate. Then she ate supper and went to bed.

The next morning she heard a great noise in the yard. When she opened the door, the geese came running to her.

"Honk, honk!" said the big gander, flapping his wings.

"Honk, honk!" said all the other geese, flapping their wings.

Everywhere she went, the twelve geese followed her, saying, "Honk, honk!" and flapping their wings.

"Dear me," said the Little Old Woman, "I do believe they want something to eat. I must buy them some corn." So she went to the market and bought a bag of corn for the geese.

Every morning when she opened the door the geese came running to her.

"Honk, honk!" they said, flapping their wings.

Then she remembered to give them some corn.

The geese ate so much corn that pretty soon the Little Old Woman had to buy another bag of corn. After a while, that bag was empty, too, and she had to buy another bag of corn.

"These geese eat a lot of corn," she said, "but after all, they are growing bigger and bigger. Their feathers are growing thicker and thicker. They will make me a fine feather bed when winter comes."

26

By and by the nights began to grow cold. The red flannel blanket was so full of holes that it did not keep the Little Old Woman warm. She shivered all night long.

"Winter will soon be here," she thought. "It is high time I clipped the geese and made my feather bed."

The next morning she went out to clip the geese.

"How warm and contented they look," said the Little Old Woman. "They will be cold if I clip their feathers. Maybe if I cut the holes out of the red blanket, it will be warm enough for me."

But when she fetched her scissors and cut the holes out of the red blanket, the holes were still there. In fact, they were bigger than ever.

"What am I to do?" she thought. "If I take their feathers, the geese will be cold. If I do not take their feathers, I will be cold. I suppose I had better use my head."

And here is how the Little Old Woman used her head. First she tied a wet towel around her forehead. Then she sat down with her forefinger against her nose and shut her eyes.

She used her head and used her head and used her head. She used her head so long that it began to ache, but finally she knew what to do.

"The red blanket is no good to me," she said. "I will cut it into twelve pieces and make each of the geese a warm red coat. Then I can clip their feathers to make myself a feather bed."

The Little Old Woman set to work and made each of the geese a little red coat. On each coat she sewed three shiny brass buttons.

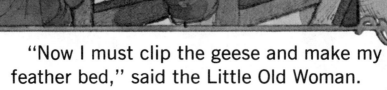

"Now I must clip the geese and make my feather bed," said the Little Old Woman.

She took a basket and went out to clip the geese. She clipped the big gander and put his feathers in the basket. She clipped the gray goose and put her feathers into the basket. Then she clipped the other geese and put their feathers into the basket.

28

When all the geese were clipped, the Little
Old Woman put a little red coat on each goose
and fastened it with the shiny brass buttons.

"How handsome the geese look," she said. "I
was very clever to think of making the little red
coats to keep them warm."
Then she carried the basket of feathers into
the house and sewed them into a strong ticking
to make a feather bed.

When the bed was all finished, the Little Old Woman said to herself, "I shall sleep very warm this winter. How wise I was to buy a flock of geese to make a feather bed. It all comes of using my head."

What Do You Think?

1. Which sentence tells the main idea of this story? Which sentences are details about the main idea?
    a. The woman cut holes out of her blanket.
    b. The woman found a way to get a feather bed.
    c. The woman bought some geese.
2. Finish each of these sentences.
    a. The woman bought a flock of geese because _____ .
    b. The woman cut holes out of her blanket because _____ .
    c. The woman made coats for the geese because _____ .

Activity

Find out about the different kinds of birds and the colors of their feathers.

30

Granny Gunther's Old Popper

by Frances B. Watts

One morning Mr. and Mrs. Hancock had to leave on a business trip. So their children Donna and Keith were to have breakfast next door at Granny Gunther's before going to school. Granny Gunther was not Donna and Keith's real grandmother, and they did not know her too well. But everyone in the neighborhood called her Granny.

"Oh, dear," said Donna, as they were getting ready for school, "I wish Mom and Dad had let us get our own breakfast. What will we talk about with Granny?"

"I don't know," sighed Keith. "I suppose we'll talk about the weather and dull things like that."

Soon they knocked half-heartedly on Granny's door.

From "Granny Gunther's Old Popper" by Frances B. Watts from *Jack and Jill* magazine, copyright © 1978 by The Saturday Evening Post Company, Indianapolis, Indiana. Adapted by permission of the publisher.

"Come in, Donna and Keith!" Granny shouted.

Granny stood at the kitchen table, beating up eggs to scramble. "Before you sit down," she said briskly, "would one of you please get my catcher's mitt out of the closet over there?"

The two children looked puzzled. Keith went to the closet and took out a well-worn baseball mitt. "What are you going to do with it, Granny?" he asked.

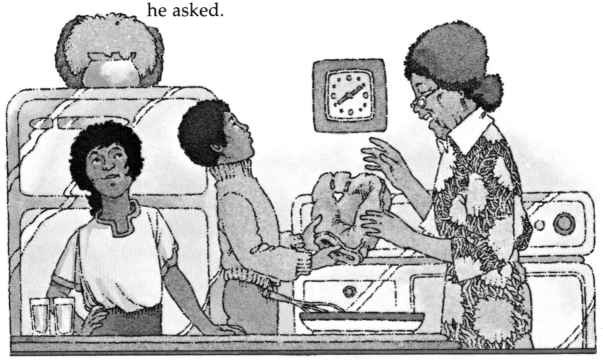

"Why, I use it when I make toast," Granny replied. "I'd burn my hands otherwise. You know how hot freshly made toast is." Then she dumped the eggs into a fry pan and began whipping them.

Donna and Keith raised their eyebrows. Who ever heard of making toast with a catcher's mitt? Why didn't she leave the toast in the toaster until it cooled off for a few seconds?

Their silent questions were answered in short order. Quickly Granny scraped the scrambled eggs onto three plates and set them on the table. Then she put a slice of toast into the pop-up toaster. Donna and Keith watched closely as Granny slipped on the baseball glove and hustled over by the door. With her eyes on the toaster and her mitt held high, she waited expectantly. All at once, the toast bounced up and sailed over toward the right window. Granny made two fast bounds, a flying leap, and caught the toast in her glove. "One out! Pop fly!" she chuckled gleefully.

Granny took the toast to the table and slapped butter on it. Then she handed the mitt to Donna. "You children might like to make your own toast," she said. "Keep an eye on it, though. It's just as apt to fly out to left field as right field."

Eagerly the children began making their toast. Donna's landed on top of the refrigerator. Keith's plopped on the floor, after he fumbled a left-handed scoop.

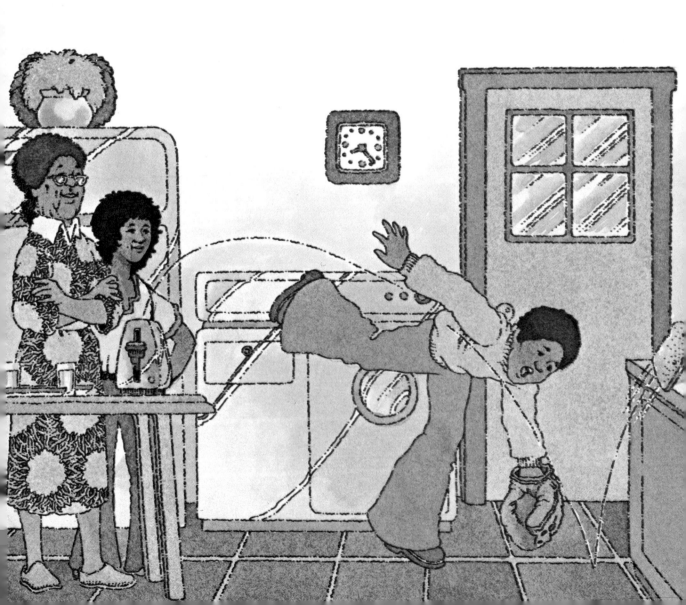

"It takes practice, children," Granny consoled them as she brushed off Keith's toast with a paper towel. "It took me weeks of practice until I got the hang of it."

"Granny, what is wrong with your toaster?" Keith asked as they started their meal.

"Nothing!" she snapped. "It makes dandy toast. It's just old, that's all. What's wrong with that?"

"Well," said Donna, "it shouldn't send the toast flying around like that. Our toaster pops the toast up gently."

"Most of them do," Granny agreed. "But in its later years Old Popper's gotten flighty and temperamental. There's not a repair person who can settle it down. So I just trained myself to become a first-class toast catcher."

"Have you ever thought of buying a new toaster?" Keith inquired.

"I have, but I won't. My daughter Elba is always after me to get another one. But why should I spend my money on a new one? There's a lot of pep yet in Old Popper."

Soon other pieces of toast were made. On their third slices, Donna fielded hers beautifully over the kitchen sink, and Keith caught his with a perfect flying leap to the ceiling lamp. They didn't know when they had had such a jolly breakfast. If they hadn't had to leave for school, they might have stayed for fourth slices.

"With more practice you children will be real pros," Granny said. "After this, bring your bread over here in the morning and make your toast in Old Popper."

Donna and Keith accepted Granny's kind invitation gratefully. Within a few weeks, the children rarely made a fumble. In fact, they were almost as good at fielding toast as Granny.

Then one Saturday Donna and Keith came over later than usual to make toast. It was clear that a lot had happened at Granny's while they were still in bed. Granny was sitting drooped in a chair. Her left foot was bandaged and propped on a stool. Her daughter Elba was there, unpacking a brand-new toaster.

"Now, Mother," Elba was saying, "you must start using this new toaster. You're too old to be playing toast-baseball. I've warned you and warned you!"

"Hi, children," Granny sighed sadly when she spied Keith and Donna. "This morning I took a flying leap, fumbled the toast, sprained my ankle, and the doctor has me grounded in this chair!"

"How terrible!" the two children cried.

"You said it," Granny nodded. "But the time has come when I have to face the fact that I'm too old to be playing games with Old Popper. Elba here has brought me this shiny new toaster. It's about time, I guess."

"Well, Mother, I'm glad you're showing common sense at last," said Elba. "I'll just take Old Popper and give it to the junk dealer."

Donna and Keith grew very solemn and sad. To have Old Popper end up as junk was unthinkable. Why, Old Popper was almost like a real person, who seemed to enjoy playing games.

Suddenly, Granny straightened up. Her spunky spirit returned full force. "You'll not take Old Popper to the junk dealer, Elba!" she exclaimed. "I told these children that Old Popper will last a long time. It's still spry enough to pitch toast. And when it's not, it'll still stay here with me."

Elba smiled. "All right, Mother," she agreed. "You can use the new toaster and the children can use Old Popper."

So it was that the Hancock children made toast in Old Popper for a good many mornings to come. And it was no surprise to Granny when years later Keith became star catcher and Donna star outfielder on their junior-high baseball teams!

What Do You Think?

1. Put the following sentences in the order in which they happened in the story.
   a. Elba gave Granny a brand-new toaster.
   b. The children became star baseball players.
   c. Granny gave Old Popper to Donna and Keith.
   d. Donna and Keith knocked half-heartedly on Granny's door.
   e. Granny made a flying leap and caught the toast in her glove.
2. What words tell what kind of person Granny was?
   neighborly   clever   spunky
   lazy   peppy   boastful
3. Why do you think Granny wasn't surprised when Donna and Keith became star baseball players?
4. Why was Granny Gunther "grounded"?
5. Which word below is not a baseball term?
   fly   fielded   pitch   toast

Activity

Make up a story about a washing machine, a refrigerator, a vacuum cleaner, or another machine that starts doing strange things.

BIGFOOT
at Rock Park

a one-act puppet play
by Tim Merriman

*Tim Merriman is a ranger and naturalist in a state
park. He wants children to learn more about
protecting the natural world around them, so he
makes puppets and writes plays about preserving
nature. Here is one of his plays.*

CHARACTERS

RANGER THORNY

CHIEF RANGER FUZZY

BIGFOOT

FERN BARKER

HIKER

SETTING

A state park. Office of CHIEF RANGER FUZZY.

THORNY   *(runs into the office, trips, and falls onto* CHIEF RANGER FUZZY*'s desk):* Ranger Fuzzy, come quickly! There's been a monster in the campground, and campers are packing to go home!

FUZZY: Slow down, Thorny, slow down. What's the problem?

THORNY: Last night a camper heard someone fooling around in the trash barrel. She ran out of her tent and surprised the monster, and it scurried off into the forest. Come on, Chief, shouldn't we investigate the incident?

FUZZY: All right, Thorny, but I hope this won't be a waste of time, because I was about to read my favorite comic strip. If you're pulling my leg, I'll have you collect garbage for a month.

THORNY: I'll prove it to you, Chief, if you will just follow me. *(FUZZY and THORNY leave the office and walk quickly to the campground.)*

THORNY: This is the trash barrel, Chief.

FUZZY: The barrel is empty! What could the monster have been looking for?

THORNY: I don't know, because the trash barrel was full last night. I wonder who could have emptied it. Oh, here comes the camper who frightened the monster away.

FERN *(approaches FUZZY and THORNY):* Who is the head ranger here, please?

FUZZY: I am Chief Ranger Fuzzy, and this is my assistant, Ranger Thorny. Can you tell us what happened here last night?

FERN: Well, my name is Fern Barker. I came here to Rock Park to camp and hike, but after last night I think I'll leave.

FUZZY: Just explain exactly what happened, please.

FERN: Well, I heard a lot of noise outside my tent in the middle of the night, so I got up to see what was wrong. When I stepped out of the tent, some horrible monster ran off from the trash barrel and yelled some strange word.

FUZZY: How big do you think the monster was, Fern? Could you see it at all?

FERN: I didn't see the monster very well because it was dark. Its footprints are right over here—*(pointing at the ground near the trash barrel)*—and they are really huge!

FUZZY: Let's have a look at those footprints. *(RANGERS and FERN walk over to the trash barrel. Two huge footprints are visible in the mud near the barrel.)*

FUZZY: Oh, oh—this is what I was afraid of. Do you know who made these footprints, Thorny?

THORNY: I don't know, but it looks like someone who has two big feet.

FUZZY: Of course, it's someone with two big feet! Those are the prints of BIGFOOT!

THORNY: BIGFOOT?

FERN: BIGFOOT? What is this Bigfoot?

FUZZY: No one knows. It appears and then disappears suddenly and leaves only its huge footprints behind. It moves like a ghost in the night.

THORNY: You mean the monster wears a sheet?

FUZZY: No, Thorny, it doesn't wear a sheet!

FERN: Oh, my! I could have been hurt.

FUZZY: I don't think so, Fern, because Bigfoot never has hurt anyone. It just seems to be interested in our garbage and trash.

THORNY: I don't know why, because garbage doesn't interest me.

FUZZY: I think I know why, Thorny. Thank you, Fern, for helping us with the investigation.

FERN: Thank you, rangers. I think I'll go back home today anyway. Good-bye. (FERN *leaves.*)

FUZZY: We have big problems, Thorny. People won't want to camp here if Bigfoot stays around very long.

THORNY: What will we do, Chief?

FUZZY: We had better go back to the office and think.

          (They start back to their office. On the way they meet a frantic HIKER.)

HIKER: Help! Help! I've seen a monster!

FUZZY: Whoa, whoa, you're shaking like a leaf. Talk slowly and tell us what happened to you.

HIKER: I was hiking on Big Rock Canyon Trail, eating a candy bar, and I had just thrown the wrapper down when—

THORNY: Threw the wrapper down! That's littering. You're not supposed to throw litter down in the park.

FUZZY: Be quiet a minute, Thorny; let's hear the rest of the story.

HIKER: Well, all of a sudden I heard a booming voice yell, "Litterbug!" When I looked up, there was a hairy monster with huge feet sitting in a tree. I dropped my backpack and ran all the way back here. Go quickly, and you'll see the monster.

FUZZY *(turns to* HIKER*):* Thanks for reporting this to us, but please don't throw any more litter down. Maybe Thorny and I can catch Bigfoot right now. *(*FUZZY *and* THORNY *run off toward the Big Rock Canyon Trail.)*

THORNY: I see the hiker's backpack, but I don't see any monster though.

FUZZY: I didn't think the monster would stay around for us to catch it. Let's look for evidence.

THORNY: Look! More big footprints!

FUZZY: It's Bigfoot again. That's what I thought. I don't see any litter though.

THORNY: The pack is empty, which means that Bigfoot must have taken all of the food and trash.

FUZZY: I wonder what it does with all of that trash?

THORNY: Maybe it has a garbage collection, Chief.

FUZZY: Terrific idea, Thorny. You have just given me an idea about how to catch Bigfoot. You get a bag of garbage and trash and meet me in the campgrounds.

THORNY: All right, Chief. *(Mumbling to himself.)* Why do I always have to collect the garbage?

(About fifteen minutes later, both rangers arrive at the campgrounds.)

THORNY: What's in the bundle, Chief?

FUZZY: It's a fish net.

THORNY: Do you want me to dig some worms for fishing, Chief?

FUZZY: No, Thorny, we're going to catch Bigfoot.

THORNY: Oh, Bigfoot likes fish nets, huh?

FUZZY: No, Thorny, Bigfoot likes garbage. Pile up the garbage and trash right here, and we'll hang the net in the tree over it. When Bigfoot comes to the garbage, we'll drop the net and catch the monster.

THORNY: Now I understand.

(They hang the net over the garbage and hide in the bushes. A half hour goes by.)

THORNY: I'm hungry, Chief—I'm as hungry as a bear. Can we go and eat lunch?

FUZZY: Shhhhh! *(Footsteps are heard.)* Here comes someone now. It's Bigfoot! It's picking up some of the garbage. Quick! Pull the string, Thorny. *(THORNY jerks on the string, and the net falls on top of BIGFOOT.)*

THORNY: We got the monster! We got it, Chief! We caught Bigfoot! *(They run to the net.)* Why, Bigfoot is so little! I thought Bigfoot was supposed to be huge!

FUZZY: Its feet are, Thorny—just look at the size of them! Be careful, Thorny, maybe it bites.

THORNY: Look, Chief. Bigfoot's eating the garbage and trash!

BIGFOOT: Gubrettil!

THORNY: Bigfoot talks! I can't believe it, Bigfoot talks!

BIGFOOT: Gubrettil—not Bigfoot, thank you.

THORNY: Wow, it even gives a polite answer!

FUZZY: Gubrettil, why have you been scaring people in the park?

BIGFOOT: I'm a gubrettil, which is litterbug spelled backwards. Gubrettils pick up litter instead of throwing it down. We eat garbage and trash.

THORNY: Yeck! That sounds awful.

FUZZY: Do you mean that the people you frightened were litterbugs?

BIGFOOT: Yes, I never bother people unless they mess up the park. I clean up after messy campers and hikers.

FUZZY: It would be good if everyone were like that.

BIGFOOT: Are you going to arrest me?

FUZZY *(pausing to think):* No, I have a better idea. Thorny, give me your hat.

THORNY: My hat? Why do you want my hat? *(Handing it to* FUZZY.*)*

FUZZY: Gubrettil, I am making you a park ranger, and from now on you will be called Ranger Bigfoot. *(Gives* THORNY's *hat to* BIGFOOT.*)* You can continue helping by teaching people not to litter.

BIGFOOT: Thanks a lot, Chief. Wow, my own ranger hat! I'm going to start looking for litterbugs right now.
(BIGFOOT runs off into the woods waving the hat.)

FUZZY: Well, that really turned out all right. Ranger Bigfoot will be a lot of help to us—right, Thorny?

THORNY *(unhappily):* Bigfoot is probably perched in a tree somewhere eating my hat!

FUZZY: Look at the bright side, Thorny. With Bigfoot consuming the litter, you may never have to drive the garbage truck again. Now let's get back to work.

THORNY: I wish everyone was a gubrettil!

THE END

What Do You Think?

1. What was the problem in "Bigfoot at Rock Park"?
2. How was the problem solved?
3. Why was Bigfoot scaring people?
4. What is a gubrettil?
5. Do you think Bigfoot will make a good ranger? Why or why not?

Activities

1. Read the play aloud with your friends. You may want to use puppets to act it out.
2. Make badges for your classmates, printing the words BE A GUBRETTIL on them.

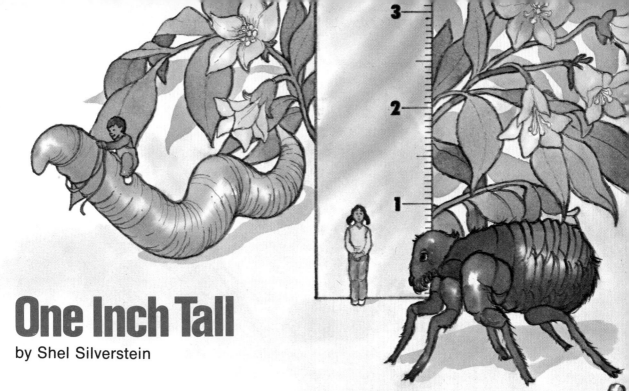

One Inch Tall

by Shel Silverstein

If you were only one inch tall, you'd ride a worm to school.
The teardrop of a crying ant would be your swimming pool.
A crumb of cake would be a feast
And last you seven days at least,
A flea would be a frightening beast
If you were one inch tall.

If you were only one inch tall, you'd walk beneath the door,
And it would take about a month to get down to the store.
A bit of fluff would be your bed,
You'd swing upon a spider's thread,
And wear a thimble on your head
If you were one inch tall.

You'd surf across the kitchen sink upon a stick of gum.
You couldn't hug your mama, you'd just have to hug her thumb.
You'd run from people's feet in fright,
To move a pen would take all night,
(This poem took fourteen years to write—
'Cause I'm just one inch tall).

Terri and the Upside-Down Teacher

by Karen O'Connor Sweeney

Terri Kawamura dashed down the path to Pine
Grove School, where she was in the third grade.
Today was special. She didn't want to be late.

"I'll prove to Mr. Burton that I can keep a
promise," she thought. "I'll keep quiet all day."
But it wouldn't be easy for Terri. She liked to talk.

54

After school yesterday Mr. Burton had told Terri, "You know, Terri, there's a time for everything. There's a time to talk and a time to get your work done. But you're not getting your work done because you spend too much time talking." He tapped his desk with a pencil as he added, "What are you going to do about it, Terri?"

Terri gulped air for courage. "I'll—I'll stop talking," she stammered. "I'll keep quiet all day tomorrow."

Mr. Burton drew a deep breath and then let it out again. "Terri Kawamura," he said, "I've heard that before."

"This time I really mean it," Terri quickly answered.

"If I could believe that, Terri, I'd—I'd— Well, I'd walk across the room on my hands—that's what I'd do!"

"You would?" Terri's eyes grew large at the thought. "You really would, Mr. Burton, in front of the whole class?"

Mr. Burton laughed. "Indeed I would."

The very thought of her teacher walking across the room on his hands sent a little shiver of delight through Terri. "I'll do it, Mr. Burton," she had promised. "I'll be quiet in school all day tomorrow."

As Terri walked to Room 6 and took her seat between Martha Jane Brill and Charles Higgins, she thought about her promise.

Later on, Mr. Burton called a group for reading. Martha Jane stopped at Terri's desk on her way to the reading table.

"Let's play jacks after lunch," Martha Jane whispered. She pulled out a shiny yellow pouch bulging with ten silver jacks and a bright red ball.

Terri nodded her head. She meant yes, but she couldn't say it.

Martha Jane wrinkled her forehead. "What's the matter?"

Mr. Burton cleared his throat and tapped the blackboard with a piece of chalk. "Is everyone ready?" Chairs squeaked. Book covers flopped open.

Mr. Burton looked over at Terri and Martha Jane. "Are you ready, Martha Jane?" he asked.

Martha Jane's face turned as red as her striped skirt. Terri squirmed. She hoped Mr. Burton wouldn't think she had broken her promise so soon.

For a second, Martha Jane frowned at Terri. Then she stuffed the jacks back into her pocket and hurried to the reading table.

Terri shook inside. She wouldn't talk—not to anyone, even her best friend, Martha Jane. Martha would understand at the end of the day. Terri enjoyed the secret promise she had made to Mr. Burton.

The morning went by fast for Terri. She finished three math sheets and two reading papers. She didn't notice the time tick by as she worked on her science project or read with her reading group. Before she knew it, the lunch bell rang. The children burst from the classroom like air from a popped balloon.

Martha rushed up to Terri. "What's going on?" she asked. "Why wouldn't you talk to me in class?"

Terri said softly, "I can't tell right now."

After lunch Martha Jane emptied her jacks from the pouch. "Cherries in the Basket or Flying Dutchman?" she asked Terri.

"I don't feel like playing," answered Terri. She was too excited to think about jacks.

Martha Jane quickly scooped up her jacks and tucked them into the yellow pouch. She glared at Terri. Just then the bell rang, and the two children hurried back to Room 6.

At two-thirty Terri looked up. "I've made it—almost," she told herself. "When Martha sees the surprise, we'll be friends again." Terri began to feel uneasy about her bargain. "If I talk in school, I'm in trouble with my teacher. If I don't, I'm in trouble with my friends."

But then a warm feeling swept over her when she thought of all the work she had finished. She hadn't done that much work in one day for a long time. Maybe Mr. Burton was right—there is a time for everything. Terri felt good.

At five minutes to three Mr. Burton called everyone together. "Class," he said, "I learned something today from Terri Kawamura."

Everyone turned to Terri. They seemed to be wondering how a third-grader could teach anyone anything.

"Terri," he continued, "taught me that she can keep a very difficult promise. She made a promise that I didn't believe she could keep. I was so sure, in fact, that I told her if she'd stop talking for one day, I'd walk across the room on my hands."

The class cheered. Terri was on the edge of her seat.

60

Mr. Burton took off his coat, hung it over his chair, and walked to the windows. "To prove I can keep a promise, too, here goes," he said.

With that, Mr. Burton popped upside down and began walking across the room on his hands. The class went wild at the sight of their upside-down teacher.

As he crossed in front of his desk, someone tapped at the door. Terri looked up. The tall figure behind the glass belonged to the principal, Mrs. Martinez.

Within seconds the door handle turned, and there stood Mrs. Martinez. Mr. Burton was still on his hands on the other side of the room. It had been too noisy for him to hear Mrs. Martinez enter.

He reached the storage closet a second later, popped right side up, and bent down to brush his trousers.

"Good afternoon, everyone," said Mrs. Martinez, looking puzzled about what was going on.

Everyone in the class held their breath to see what would happen next. Terri watched with wide eyes.

"Mrs. Martinez, I can explain," said Mr. Burton. Then he said in an excited tone, unlike his usual calm voice, "Class, sit down, please."

Mrs. Martinez tried to hide a smile. Then she burst out laughing. The entire third grade joined in.

"Mr. Burton," Mrs. Martinez said agreeably, "you'd make fine entertainment for the next P.T.A. meeting."

Martha Jane looked at Terri. They smiled at each other for the first time all afternoon.

Mr. Burton slipped into his coat and fumbled with the buttons as he spoke. "Mrs. Martinez, I don't usually do things like this. I'm very sorry—I'll try to explain—"

Mrs. Martinez smiled at Mr. Burton. "Why, you don't need to apologize, Mr. Burton. Don't you know there's a time for everything? And in third grade there's definitely a time for fun!"

Terri Kawamura let out a happy sigh. She thought, "Yes, Mr. Burton was right—there *is* a time for everything."

What Do You Think?

1. What was Terri's promise?
2. What did Mr. Burton say he would do if Terri kept her promise?
3. When Mr. Burton spoke to Martha Jane and her face "turned as red as her striped skirt," how do you think Martha Jane felt? Why do you think she felt that way?
4. How do you think Terri felt when she was able to keep her promise to Mr. Burton?
5. Think of a time when you had to keep something a secret. What happened before and after the secret was found out?

Activity

Make a list of things that you think are fun in your class.

Telling Time by Shadows

by Martha and Charles Shapp

Did you ever notice your shadow at different times of the day? Shadows change as the day goes on.

In the morning the sun makes long shadows. In the middle of the day when the sun seems to be right over your head, your shadow is very, very small. In the afternoon as the sun goes down, there are very long shadows again. But the long afternoon shadows fall a different way from the long morning shadows.

Long, long ago people told time by the shadows. They made sundials.

You can make a sundial and tell time by shadows. Put a piece of paper in the sunlight. Stand a pencil in a spool in the middle of the paper.

The shadow of the pencil will fall on the paper. The pencil's shadow will move as the day goes on. Use a watch and every hour mark the place where the shadow falls.

Now your paper is a sundial, and you can tell time every sunny day. Just look at your paper sundial and see where the shadow falls.

The King's Shadow

by Robert D. Larranaga

Once there was a little king who was afraid of
his own shadow. Sometimes he even walked
backwards to keep an eye on it, which looked
pretty silly in palace parades.

So the little king called in his three wizards and
asked them what to do.

"Tie your shadow up," said one. "Put it in a cage,"
said another. "Throw it in the fire," said a third.

67

The king was afraid to do any of these things.
After all, the shadow was attached to his feet!

"Then step out of your shoes," the wizards said.
But when the king did, his shadow still followed.

The wizards tried to paint over the king's
shadow, but all the paint in the kingdom
couldn't cover it up.

They tried to nail it to the ground, but the nails
wouldn't hold.

"It's no use, Your Majesty," they said. "You'll just
have to learn to be brave."

Instead the little king locked himself in a dark room in the castle tower, where he could hide from his shadow.

One day a messenger knocked at the door. "Your Majesty!" he cried. "There's a fiery dragon loose in your kingdom! It says it won't leave until you fight it."

"I'm m—m—m—m—m—much more afraid of a dragon than I am of my shadow," said the king.

But there was no getting around it—the dragon had to be fought. So the trembling king was dressed in a suit of shiny armor, placed on a horse, and sent out to do battle with the dragon.

Now, this was no ordinary dragon, or an ordinary knight could have slain it. It was twice the size of a house, and it had a terrible, terrible temper!

The dragon had spent the whole day breathing fire on haystacks and knocking over trees with its tail. But it wasn't the least bit tired. It was ready and waiting for the king.

Naturally, the king got off to a late start. He wanted the sun behind his back so he could keep an eye on his shadow while he rode along.

As the sun sank lower and lower, the king's shadow grew longer and longer. Finally the shadow stretched two hundred feet in front of him.

When the dragon saw the shadow creeping over the hill, it began to snort and breathe out fire.

But its snorts turned to shudders, and its fire turned to smoke when it saw the size of the shadow.

70

Thinking that a giant had been sent to slay it, the dragon turned and fled.

"Well, how do you like that?" said the king. "That dragon fled at the sight of me!"

And the little king turned around and headed back to the castle without once looking to see where his shadow was.

After all, why worry about a shadow when you've just chased a fiery dragon?

What Do You Think?

1. What was the king's problem at the beginning of "The King's Shadow"? How was that problem solved?

2. In the sentence below, what does the underlined part mean?
   The king wanted the sun behind his back so he could <u>keep an eye on</u> his shadow while he rode along.

3. Is "The King's Shadow" about things that have been made up or is it about things that are true? How do you know?

4. Is "Telling Time by Shadows" about things that have been made up or is it about things that are true? How do you know?

Activities

1. Follow the directions in "Telling Time by Shadows" to make a sundial. On a sunny day use the sundial to tell the time.

2. Play shadow tag. One player is It and tags another player by stepping on that player's shadow. The player whose shadow was tagged then becomes It.

Rod-and-Reel Trouble

by Bobbi Katz

"How about helping me catch some fish today?"
Chris asked his cousin, Lori. "We can go to the
creek. The trout are really jumping."

Lori was looking at a shining-new fishing rod
displayed in the window. More than anything in
the world, Lori loved to go trout fishing.

"It's a deal!" she said. "We don't want any
jumping trout to get away!"

The creek was dangerous because its banks were steep, and the water ran swiftly at this time of year. The stones were so smooth and slippery, it was easy to fall. The creek was out-of-bounds for Lori, and she could only go there with a grown-up. But Chris was almost grown-up.

"You go home to get your gear and meet me back here by four," said Chris.

"Don't forget your socks," Lori reminded him.

Lori and Chris wore rubber hip boots for trout fishing, but boots weren't enough. The water was so cold that they needed warm socks, and Chris usually forgot his.

Lori rushed home and pulled on her warm slacks. "I'm going fishing, Mom!" she said.

Her mother spotted Lori's hip boots, which meant fishing in the creek.

"Fishing where and with whom?" her mother asked.

"Down at the creek with Chris," Lori answered, and held her breath.

"Chris and who else?" her mother asked.

"Chris is sixteen, Mom, so please, can't I go? He's waiting, and I'm late."

"All right," her mother said, "but next time ask me before you make plans. And, Lori, don't lose track of time. Dad shouldn't have to come and get you for dinner."

Lori tossed her boots and tackle box in the basket of her bike. Carefully balancing her rod, she rode over to Clark's store.

Chris and Lori arrived at the store at the same time, and together they rode down to the creek.

Chris scrambled down the steep slope, and Lori followed. They stood at the edge of the creek. The rushing water drowned out all other sounds so that they could not even hear the highway traffic.

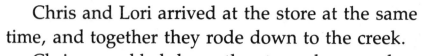

Quickly the two pulled off their sneakers. "Oh, no!" said Lori. "This time *I* forgot my warm socks!"

"OK, Smarty," said Chris, "so this time you'll have the cold toes."

Chris took a lure from his tackle box, cast his line, and waded into the water.

Lori opened her tackle box and looked over her lures. She'd try to land a fish from shore.

76

Lori hooked a lure on her line, cast, and within seconds felt a pull. She forgot her idea to stay out of the water as she carefully waded into the middle of the creek.

She played the trout's own game as she tightened and slackened the line. When the fish slowed down, she reeled it in. The trout was pulling now, fighting for its life. It grew harder to turn the reel—Lori's arms ached.

"Stay with it, Lori," Chris shouted over the roaring waters.

Lori turned the reel with all her might, and there it was! A beauty—the biggest fish she'd ever caught!

Seeing the fish seemed to give Lori new energy as she quickly tightened the last bit of line. Before she knew it, she was standing on the shore, holding the trout.

"Good going," said Chris, wading over to her. He carefully removed the lure from the fish's mouth. Then he put the fish on a chain, looping the chain around a thin stump. The trout dangled in the water.

The trout was a real rainbow with its body looking like trapped sunlight. It was the most beautiful thing Lori had ever seen.

"Chris," Lori said, "you know something? I really love that fish."

"I know what you mean," Chris said. "There is something special about a fish you catch yourself."

Chris started to wade back into the creek. "Look, Lori," he shouted, "a water snake." Chris started to follow the snake.

"Yuk, snakes," said Lori to herself. Chris was interested in them. He'd catch one, study it, and let it go. Lori wasn't afraid of snakes—she just didn't like them.

"I got it!" shouted Chris as he leaned over. Splash! He fell into the water.

At first Lori laughed. "Serves you right!" she said, but Chris wasn't getting up.

"Chris! Stop fooling!" she shouted as she waded into the water.

Chris's head was halfway under water, and the water was turning red.

Lori threw down her rod as she tried to pull Chris up, but his limp body was too heavy for her. The best she could do was to kneel down and prop up his head. Chris must have hit his head against a rock because there was a big cut on his forehead.

"Help! Help!" she screamed. But Lori knew that no one could hear her because the rushing water drowned out all other sounds.

Lori pressed her hand against the cut as hard as she could. Little by little the bleeding slowed.

She watched the current carry her rod downstream. It didn't seem very important.

By this time Lori was freezing, and her legs felt numb. Chris's eyes flickered open and shut, but he didn't seem to see her.

It was getting dark. A million years seemed to pass before Lori heard a voice. "Lori! Lori!" shouted her father.

"Dad!" she screamed with all her might.

Her father came running along the shore. "Lori," he called. "Are you hurt? Can't you move?"

"It's Chris—he's hurt bad; I can't let go of him."

Her father waded into the creek, shoes and all. He took one look at Chris and said, "We need to fix that cut now, Lori! Can you hold him a little longer?"

Lori nodded even though she felt as if all her strength was gone.

Her father pulled off his jacket and spread it over her shoulders, but the jacket slid into the water. Next he tore two long strips from one of his shirt sleeves. He folded one strip into a square and pressed it against Chris's cut. With Lori's help, he quickly wrapped the other strip around Chris's head. Then he lifted the boy out of the water.

"Can you get up?" her father asked Lori.

Lori tried to stand, but her cramped legs wouldn't move.

"Let me get Chris ashore," her father said. "I'll be back for you."

Lori nodded. She felt light-headed, but she could wait.

Her father waded to the shore and lowered Chris to the bank of the creek. Then he waded in again.

Lori was slumped in the water, half alive. Her father lifted her and carried her dripping to the shore.

82

"Stay awake, Lori," her father pleaded as he rubbed her cold face and hands. "You have to stay awake because I have to get help. Talk to Chris, just keep talking."

A little color returned to Lori's face. "I'll try," she whispered.

Her father climbed the slope. It was growing darker as he hurried to his car. When he got to the car, he turned on the flashing lights and then found a flashlight in the glove compartment. He looked through the trunk for an old blanket.

Within seconds a tow truck pulled over. Lori's father told the driver what had happened.

"Here, take my jacket," said the driver. "I'll use my two-way radio to get an ambulance."

Lori's father hurried back to Lori and Chris. He wrapped Chris in the blanket and Lori in the jacket. Before long he could hear the ambulance siren wailing over the sound of rushing water.

"My trout, my trout," mumbled Lori, while the ambulance crew lifted her onto a stretcher.

The ambulance rushed the two friends to the hospital. By the time they had arrived, they both were awake. Chris looked at Lori. He reached over and squeezed her hand. What can you say to someone who saved your life?

What Do You Think?
1. Why didn't Lori's mother want Lori to go to the creek? What made her mother change her mind?
2. How did Chris get in trouble at the creek?
3. How did Lori save Chris's life?
4. Why do you think Lori's father showed up in time to rescue Lori and Chris?
5. What is the meaning of *reel* in this sentence?
   She saw him reel when the baseball struck him.
   a. roller or spool for winding a fishing line
   b. sway under a blow or shock

Activities
1. Write another ending for this story. Tell what Chris said when he learned Lori had saved his life. Tell how Lori felt about losing her prize catch.
2. Find out the kinds of fish or snakes in your area.

84

Dorsey, U.S. Mail Dog

by Jane K. Priewe

Years ago, a hungry, thirsty dog wandered on sore feet out of the desert into a silver-mining town. Mr. Stacey, the postmaster of Calico, California, was sorry for the starving dog. He fed the animal and gave him water.

"Now, get!" Mr. Stacey said, after the skinny dog had gobbled up the food and lapped up all the water. "Go on! I don't need a dog!"

Mr. Stacey found that what you think you don't need is sometimes what you get, because the dog would not leave. He whined and crawled up to Mr. Stacey. The dog's soft brown eyes pleaded so hard for kindness that the postmaster laughed and patted the black-and-white head.

"All right, you can stay," Mr. Stacey said, chuckling. "And since you have no name, I'll call you Dorsey."

Dorsey wagged his tail and trotted behind his new friend into the little wooden post-office building.

"We have to take the mail over to East Calico," Mr. Stacey said the next morning. "If you're going to be my dog, you must get used to taking this seven-mile hike three times a week. Come on, Dorsey."

Mr. Stacey packed letters, newspapers, and magazines into a leather mail pouch. He stepped outside into the broiling sun. As he ambled up the main street of Calico, he called a greeting to some people on the porch of the general store. Dorsey trotted at his heels.

"Who's your friend, Stacey?" one of the people laughed, pointing to the small shepherd dog. "Are you taking him with you to East Calico in hopes of losing him?"

"I'm calling him Dorsey, and he's my new helper. He'll be company for me when I hike to the Bismark Mine," said Mr. Stacey.

Mr. Stacey walked on. "Dorsey," he said, "you're going to be fine company, because you can't talk back." The man laughed softly and stopped to pat the dog's head. Dorsey danced a happy circle around Mr. Stacey and they continued on their way. First they dropped off the mail at the Maggie Mine in Calico. Then they went on their way with the mail for East Calico and the Bismark Mine.

For months Dorsey didn't miss a delivery with Mr. Stacey. Then one morning Mr. Stacey woke up aching all over. He groaned and rolled over in bed. Dorsey, who slept on the floor nearby, whined and licked the hand that dangled over the edge of the bed.

Mr. Stacey groaned again. The mail had to be delivered. He wondered how he would manage. Then Dorsey put his front feet on the bed and looked at his friend.

"I wonder—could I trust *you* to carry the mail, Dorsey?" Mr. Stacey rubbed the dog's head. "You've been there often enough, and you're a smart dog. Remember that time a letter fell out of the mail pouch, and you found it and brought it to me? I wonder if . . . ."

Dorsey barked, wagged his tail, and aimed a wet kiss at Mr. Stacey's face.

"Now cut that mush out!" Mr. Stacey sat up, holding his head. "I'm going to trust you, Dorsey, so I'll strap the pouch on you, and hope you're as smart as I think you are. I'll send a note with you, telling the people at the Bismark Mine to return some mail if you make the trip all right."

A little later Mr. Stacey went to the door with Dorsey and headed the dog toward East Calico. Dorsey took off up the dirt street as if a mountain lion were after him.

Dorsey made the trip just fine, so Mr. Stacey decided to send Dorsey with the mail more often. The dog made the trip much more quickly than the man. And Dorsey never failed to get the mail through. Many times, miners came into Calico laughing. They told how they had tried to head Dorsey off on the trail. The dog seemed to sense that the miners were there. Dorsey always made a wide circle around the place the miners were hidden. Then he came back onto the trail farther along the way.

90

Mr. Stacey had a little harness made with a saddlebag on both sides. The harness could be strapped on Dorsey, and each saddlebag had U.S. MAIL printed on it in big, white letters.

For three years the small shepherd dog traveled back and forth between Calico and the Bismark Mine in East Calico. To the miners, Dorsey was an important part of their lives, because he was *their* mail dog.

What Do You Think?
1. How did Mr. Stacey first meet Dorsey?
2. Why did Dorsey begin delivering the mail?
3. Why did Mr. Stacey think Dorsey could deliver the mail?
4. How did Mr. Stacey make sure Dorsey delivered the mail?
5. The picture map on page 92 shows some of the buildings in Calico, California, where Dorsey delivered mail many years ago. You can still see this town, which has been restored. The line with the arrows shows the route that Dorsey may have taken to deliver the mail. Use the map to answer the questions on page 92.

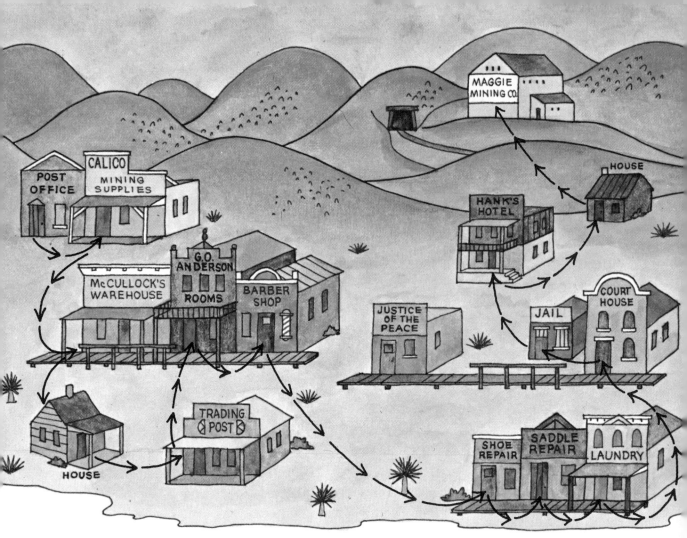

a. Dorsey left the post office to deliver the mail. Where did he go first? second? third?
b. Where did Dorsey go after he delivered the mail at the barber shop?
c. Dorsey did not stop at one place to deliver the mail. What place did he pass by?
d. Where did Dorsey go after he left the laundry?
e. Where was the last place Dorsey delivered his mail?

Activity

Write a letter to a friend.

92

The Story of King Midas

a Greek myth
retold by Beatrice Alexander

Long, long ago there lived a king named Midas. He had a shining palace, and goblets and plates of gold and silver, and servants to do his bidding. He had a good wife, a little daughter whom he adored, a yellow-eyed cat, and enough money to buy almost anything else he wanted.

And yet this foolish king was not very happy. He was miserly—he loved money for its own sake, and he liked to look at it and to touch it. In a secret room at the top of his palace he kept all his gold. He liked nothing better than to sit in this little room, take out his coins, and count them over and over again.

One day, while he was doing this, he felt that there was someone standing behind him. He turned sharply—there was no one there. But a tall shadow showed in the block of sunlight that lay on the floor, and, by this, Midas knew that he must have a visitor from the gods.

"Midas," said a voice, "I have come to give you whatever you wish for most. But mind you, you may choose just once."

"If you please," Midas said, "I should like to see everything I touch turn into gold for me."

The voice replied, "In the morning when you wake, this gift shall be yours." With that the shadow faded away.

When Midas awoke the next morning, he poked a finger at the bedpost. He could hardly believe his eyes when it promptly turned into shining gold. He lifted up his slippers, and they too turned to gold, with the creases still in them and the lining wrinkled in one. To be sure, when he put them on, they were not very comfortable, but rather hard and stiff. Still, they were far prettier than they had been—at least in Midas's eyes.

Midas went for a walk in his garden before breakfast and tried his gift on some of the flowers. A rose and a daisy turned to gold just like that—and Midas was pleased with the results.

He managed to get a good many flowers changed before breakfast. As Midas sat at the table, he looked through the window at the flowers and thought them a very pretty sight indeed. He tried to open the thin curtain to see better, and the curtain promptly turned to gold, cutting off his view and the sunlight.

In came a servant with his meal. Midas looked with pleasure on the white crusty bread and silver platter piled high with grapes and apples, for he was hungry and thirsty.

He broke off a few green grapes and popped them into his mouth—and as quickly popped them out again. Instead of the sweet grape flesh, his teeth had bit on hard little golden bullets. He reached for the bread—and the whole loaf became a great lump of gold.

Midas was frightened. How was he ever to get anything to eat? As he was thinking about this, the yellow-eyed cat jumped on his knee, purring. Midas laid his hand on its soft, striped fur. Suddenly he looked down in horror at the feel of the stiff little golden hairs along its back.

As the king looked sadly down at the little cat, he felt two soft hands over his head. Chuckling, he turned in his chair and seized his daughter's fingers—and then he saw the laughing little girl turn into a golden statue.

Poor Midas! He wept, begging to be delivered from this horrible golden gift.

The gods heard him and took pity on him. A voice spoke to him and said, "Go down to the river and wash your hands well. The water will carry this gift of yours away. Then bring some of the water in a jug, and with it change back again what you have lost."

Midas ran as fast as he could to the river which was nearby, and washed his hands again and again in its water. As the gods had promised, the gift of gold left him. He filled the jug which he had brought, ran back with it, and poured water on the golden statue. In a twinkling it was again his own dear rosy-cheeked daughter, laughing and running about the room. With wet hands he stroked the little cat. Its fur immediately became fur again—but the little cat tore from the room, for it did not like the feel of water! Then Midas and his little daughter turned the golden food back into real food and ate it. After that they walked in the garden and turned the golden flowers into real flowers once more.

And forever after Midas said that the lowly weeds in the meadow were more to him than a hundred thousand gold coins.

Section Two

Stone Soup for Supper

by Johanna Hurwitz

Tuesday night there was spaghetti and meatballs for supper. Dad was out of town attending a business conference, and so as a treat Mom made the children's favorite meal. Nora ate two portions, and Teddy ate three. They both had red beards and mustaches and full stomachs when they finished.

On Wednesday Teddy announced, "Tonight I want you to cook my favorite food."

"I thought spaghetti was your favorite," said Mom.

"Not anymore. It's Nora's favorite, not mine. Tonight I want mine," demanded Teddy.

"OK," agreed Mom. She thought Teddy would ask for hot dogs or French toast. But he surprised her.

"I want stone soup," he said.

"Stone soup! That's just a story," Mom said, laughing. "The three soldiers only pretend that they can make soup from a stone to trick the people into sharing their food. Everyone gives something for seasoning, and soon there's a big pot of soup. Don't you remember? I can't really make it. Besides, how do you know it's your favorite? You don't eat any vegetables. Stone soup has lots of vegetables."

"I love vegetables in stone soup," said Teddy.

"Well, we don't even have any stones," explained Mom. "Besides, it's raining outside so we can't go to the park to look for stones."

"We have a stone!" cried Nora. She had been sitting very quietly listening to Teddy's discussion with Mom. Now she ran to the bedroom. On Dad's desk was a large, smooth stone picked up on a beach in Maine.

Teddy ran to his bedroom and returned with the library book called *Stone Soup* that Mom had read at bedtime the night before. "Here is the cookbook," he called out.

"That's not a cookbook," said Mom, but she opened the book and began mumbling to herself about onions, carrots, potatoes. . . .

Mom went to the refrigerator and took out some carrots. "I think I'm all out of onions," she remembered. "Nora, you can go upstairs and ask Mrs. Wurmbrand if we may borrow two onions."

"I want to go!" shouted Teddy.

"All right, go together," said Mom. "You can take this measuring cup and stop at the Michaelses' too. Ask Mrs. Michaels if she has any barley. And remember, don't ring the doorbell. Just knock softly. Little Russell may be asleep. It's time for his afternoon nap."

Nora and Teddy didn't wait for the elevator. They ran up the one flight of stairs to the eighth floor. They rang Mrs. Wurmbrand's bell and waited for her slow steps.

Nora said to Teddy, "Let's invite Mrs. Wurmbrand to have soup because she is going to lend us food. We'll invite the Michaelses too."

Downstairs Mom scrubbed the stone that had been sitting as a paperweight on Dad's desk all these years.

A half hour passed before the children returned with the onions and barley.

Mom cut up the onions and put them in her largest pot, which was already filled with boiling water and the stone. Both children climbed up on chairs to peek inside the pot. Next Mom cut up the carrots.

"Did you remember to put in salt and pepper?" asked Teddy. He had a good memory.

Mom put in the pepper and the barley.

"I have powdered mashed potatoes, potato chips, and frozen French fries," she told Nora and Teddy. "I don't have any real potatoes. Shall we just leave them out?"

"Oh, no!" the children protested. "We can't leave anything out."

"Let's borrow some from Anita," suggested Nora. Anita was another neighbor. She lived by herself in a tiny apartment. So off went the children across the hall to borrow the potatoes.

They returned with potatoes and also a small bag of mushrooms.

"Anita said these were left over from the dinner she cooked last night," Nora explained.

"I don't know who would have cabbage," said Mom. But then she answered herself. "Yes, I do! Mrs. Jones was in line behind me at the supermarket yesterday. She had a head of cabbage in her cart. Go and ask her if she could spare us a few leaves from it."

Before long the children returned with some of Mrs. Jones's cabbage. It was added to the pot, together with a piece of meat cut off from the pot roast Mom was going to cook the next night when Dad came home.

All afternoon the children took turns helping Mom stir the pot. The kitchen had a lovely smell. It wasn't carrots or potatoes or meat or barley or cabbage; it was stone soup.

At six o'clock, as Mom was just about to serve supper, the doorbell rang.

It was Mr. and Mrs. Michaels with Russell. "It was so nice of you to invite us to have supper with you. I love spur-of-the-moment invitations. They are the most fun!" Mrs. Michaels handed Mom a package of ice cream. "I had this in the freezer, and I thought I would contribute it to the meal."

As they stood at the open door, the elevator door opened too. Mrs. Wurmbrand stepped out. She was wearing her best dress. "You are kind to invite me to dinner on such a rainy, gloomy day," she said, handing Mom a box of cookies in a lovely tin.

Mom looked very surprised. But she was also very polite. "Let's all come inside," she said.

The guests came in, and Mom rushed to get some more bowls. "I hadn't finished setting the table," she explained.

The doorbell rang. It was Anita with a jar of olives. "I can't stay long. I have a date in about an hour," she apologized.

After Anita came in, Mr. and Mrs. Jones arrived. Mrs. Jones carried a steaming platter of meat. "This was already in the oven when your children came downstairs," explained Mrs. Jones. "It tastes so much better hot. I hope you don't mind that I brought it."

Mom looked at the platter. The meat was surrounded by brown potatoes. Mr. Jones stood next to his wife holding a pitcher of gravy.

The Joneses went into the dining room and greeted the other guests. Teddy was sitting on his high stool grinning happily and Nora was handing out paper napkins when the doorbell rang again.

"Who else is coming?" Mom whispered to Nora.

"I don't know. We didn't ask anyone else," Nora said. Mom went to the door and opened it. It was Dad!

"Surprise!" he said. "I was able to get away from the conference early."

"We have a surprise too," said Nora and Teddy, hugging Dad. "We are having stone soup for supper!"

"And company," added Mom.

"It is just like in the book," said Teddy. "And I will eat all the vegetables," he promised.

What Do You Think?

1. Which sentence tells the main idea of the story? Which sentences are details about the main idea?
   a. Teddy's family and neighbors all ate supper together.
   b. Teddy's mother read "Stone Soup" to him.
   c. Teddy's family and neighbors all helped to make stone soup.
   d. Father came home early from his business trip.
2. How do you know that the children's invitation to the neighbors was a complete surprise to Mom?
3. What was used to make stone soup?

Activity

Make up a recipe for soup. Tell what you would need and how to cook it.

WAGON WHEELS

by Barbara Brenner

In 1878 the Muldie family left their home in Kentucky to travel to Nicodemus, Kansas, where free land was being offered by the United States government.

A schoolteacher in Nicodemus heard about the adventures of the Muldie boys and wrote the story down. Her family gave the story to Barbara Brenner, who wrote a book about the Muldie boys.

"There it is, boys," Daddy said. "Across this river is Nicodemus, Kansas. That is where we are going to build our house. There is free land for everyone here in the West. All we have to do is go and get it."

We had come a long way to get to Kansas, all the way from Kentucky. It had been a hard trip and a sad one—Mama died on the way. Now there were just the four of us—Daddy, Willie, Little Brother, and me, Johnny.

"Come on, boys," Daddy called. "Let's put our feet on free dirt."

We crossed the river, wagon and all. A man was waiting for us on the other side. "I am Sam Hickman," he said. "Welcome to the town of Nicodemus."

"Why, thank you, brother," Daddy said. "But where *is* your town?"

"Right here," Mr. Hickman said.

We did not see any houses, but we saw smoke coming out of holes in the prairie.

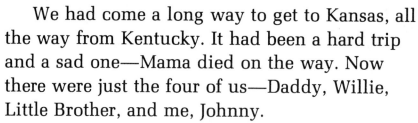

"Holes in the ground are for rabbits and snakes, not for people," my daddy said. "I am a carpenter, and I can build fine wood houses for this town."

"There's no time to build wood houses now," Mr. Hickman told my daddy. "Winter is coming, and winter in Kansas is *mean*. You'd better get yourself a dugout before the ground freezes."

Daddy knew Sam Hickman was right, so we got our shovels and we dug a dugout. It wasn't much of a place—it had a dirt floor, dirt walls, no windows, and a roof made of grass and branches. But we were glad to have that dugout when the wind began to whistle across the prairie.

Every night Willie lit the lamp and made a fire. I cooked a rabbit stew or fried a pan of fish fresh from the river.

After supper Daddy would always say, "How about a song or two?" He would take out his banjo and *plink-a-plunk! plink-a-plunk!* Pretty soon that dugout felt like home.

Winter came, and that Kansas winter *was* mean. It snowed day after day so that we could not hunt or fish. We had no more rabbit stew and no more fish fresh from the river. All we had to eat was cornmeal mush.

Then one day there was no more cornmeal. There was not a lick of food in the whole town of Nicodemus, and nothing left to burn for firewood. Little Brother cried all the time—he was so cold and hungry.

Daddy wrapped blankets around him. "Hush, baby son," he said to him. "Try to sleep. The supply train will be coming soon."

But the supply train did not come, not that day nor the next. On the third day we heard the sound of horses. Daddy looked out to see who it was. "Indians!" he said.

We were scared because we had all heard stories about Indians. We watched from the dugout. Everyone in Nicodemus was watching the Indians.

First the Indians made a circle, and then they took things from their saddlebags and dropped them on the ground. The Indians turned and rode straight toward the dugouts.

"Now they are coming for us!" Willie cried.

But the Indians rode right past us and kept on going.

We waited a long time to be sure they were gone. Then everyone ran out into the snow to see what the Indians had left. It was FOOD!

Everyone talked at once.

"Look!"

"Fresh deer meat!"

"Fish!"

"Dried beans and squash!"

"And bundles of sticks to keep our fires burning!"

There was a feast in Nicodemus that night. Before we ate, Daddy said to us, "Johnny, Willie, Little Brother, I want you to remember this day. Never forget that the Osage Indians saved our lives in Nicodemus."

Finally spring came. One day in late March Daddy announced, "Boys, this prairie is too flat for me. I want to find land with trees and hills, so I'm going to look for a new place for us."

I said, "I will start loading the wagon."

But Daddy said, "Hold on, now. I want you boys to stay—you have shelter and friends here. I will go alone and send for you when I find a place."

I was scared to stay alone, and so was Willie. Poor Little Brother—he tried to understand what Daddy was saying.

We all listened as Daddy told us, "I will leave cornmeal for your bread and salt for your meat and some molasses for a sweet. You be good boys, you hear? Take care of Little Brother, and never let him out of your sight." There were tears in Daddy's eyes when he said good-by to us.

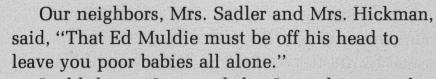

Our neighbors, Mrs. Sadler and Mrs. Hickman, said, "That Ed Muldie must be off his head to leave you poor babies all alone."

I told them, "I am no baby. I am eleven, and Willie is eight. We can take care of ourselves. Little Brother is only three, but we can take care of him too."

We did what our daddy had told us—we hunted and fished and cooked and swept the dugout clean. We even baked our own cornbread.

We never let Little Brother out of our sight. We made him a wagon out of an old box. Mrs. Sadler gave us wheels for it. We put Little Brother in the wagon and pulled him along with us. You could hear the wheels squeak a mile away. When people in Nicodemus heard that sound, they always said, "There go the Muldie boys."

One day we were picking berries near the river. Willie said, "Johnny, I smell smoke."

We looked up—the whole sky was orange. We heard someone shout, "Prairie fire!" We saw the fire behind us—it was coming fast.

"We will be burned up," Willie cried. "There is no place to run!"

I saw a deer running toward the river. "Quick!" I told Willie. "Run to the river!"

We ran, pulling the wagon with Little Brother behind us. People from Nicodemus were running with us now. When we got to the water, I told Willie, "Jump in. Hold the wagon. I will hold Little Brother."

Everyone was jumping in around us. Mr. Hickman helped me hold Little Brother, and another neighbor, Mr. Hill, helped Willie with the wagon.

There was fire and smoke all around, but the water kept the fire from us. We stayed there for a long time. When the fire had died out, we all walked home.

April went by, then May and June. We hunted and fished and waited for a letter from Daddy, but nothing came. Then in July the postrider came with a letter for us. It said:

Dear boys,

I have found fine, free land near Solomon City. There is wood to build a house and good black dirt for growing corn and beans. There is a map with this letter. The map shows where I am and where you are. Follow the map. Stay close to the Solomon River until you come to a deer trail, and you will find me. I know you can do it because you are my fine big boys.

Love to you all,
Daddy

We started out the next day. We piled cornbread and blankets into Little Brother's wagon until there was no room for Little Brother.

"Can you walk like a big boy?" I asked him. He nodded.

All of Nicodemus came out to say good-by.
They said, "Poor babies. Going a hundred-and-fifty
miles all by themselves." But we knew we could do
it because our daddy had told us we could.

We went to the river, and we followed the
map. We walked all day. When Little Brother got
tired, I carried him.

At night we stopped and made a fire. I told
Willie, "We will take turns. First I will watch the
fire, and you sleep. Then it will be your turn to
watch. Fire the gun sometimes. It will scare wild
animals away."

There were plenty of wild animals on the
prairie—wolves, panthers, and coyotes. Each night
our fire and the sound of the gun kept them away.

For twenty-two days we followed the river. Then one day we came to a deer trail. It led away from the river, just as it did on the map. "This way," I told my brothers.

We walked along the trail, which led up a hill. On the side of the hill we saw a little house with a garden in front. We could see corn growing. A man came out of the house. When he saw us, he began to run toward us.

"Willie! Johnny! Little Brother!"

"Daddy!"

There was such hugging and kissing and talking and crying and laughing and singing that I bet they heard us all the way back in Nicodemus! Mrs. Sadler must have said, "Sounds like the Muldie boys have found their daddy!"

What Do You Think?

1. Did this story really happen? How do you know?
2. Finish each of these sentences.
   a. The Muldie family dug a dugout house because ____.
   b. The people of Nicodemus were saved from starvation because ____.
   c. When spring came, Daddy left because ____.
   d. The boys were able to find Daddy because ____.
3. Why was a dugout a good place to live?
4. How did Johnny and Willie feel when Daddy told them he was going to find a new place to live?
5. In what state did the Muldie family finally settle?

Activity

Get a map of your state and find where you live.

Old Log House

by James S. Tippett

On a little green knoll
At the edge of the wood
My great great grandmother's
First house stood.

The house was of logs,
My grandmother said,
With one big room
And a lean-to shed.

The logs were cut
And the house was raised
By pioneer men
In olden days.

I like to hear
My grandmother tell
How they built the fireplace
And dug the well.

They split the shingles;
They filled each chink;
It's a house of which
I like to think.

Forever and ever
I wish I could
Live in a house
At the edge of the wood.

A FOREST TRAIL

by Sue Massey

Estrell, Alfredo, and Stephanie strolled through the forest preserve. Suddenly they stopped and jumped up and down while they clapped their hands over their heads ten times. Then they stood still for a moment before they walked on.

Do you think they were behaving strangely? Estrell, Alfredo, and Stephanie wouldn't think so. That is the way everyone behaves on this very special trail called a physical fitness trail.

The first time they visited the forest preserve they got an explanation of the trail from the forest ranger. "It's a path that you run or walk along," said the ranger. "Look, here's a map of our trail. It's a mile long."

"What are all those circles on the map?" asked Alfredo.

"Those are exercise stations," answered the ranger. "That's where you stop running and do an exercise. There are twenty stations on this trail, and each one helps you develop a different set of muscles."

"What kinds of exercises are there?" asked Estrell.

"Well, each station has a sign that shows you what exercise to do," explained the ranger.

Finally, when the ranger had answered all their questions, the children started down the trail.

Together, they read the first sign. "Jumping Jacks," read Stephanie. "I know how to do them. You jump up and down and clap your hands over your head. Let's do some."

So they all did jumping jacks and then they ran on to Station 2. "This is called the High Chair, but there's no seat in the chair," said Estrell. "Let me try first."

She supported herself on the arms of the chair and slowly brought her legs up, with her knees held straight. "Oh, this is hard!" she exclaimed. "I can do only two of these."

Luckily, Station 3 was easier. It was a Log Jump, and the children jumped right up to Station 4.

Estrell, Alfredo, and
Stephanie spent a long time at
Station 4 doing Hip Circles.
They hung from the rings while
they kept their feet firmly on
the ground. Then they swung
their hips in big circles. All of a
sudden Stephanie started to giggle and said, "We
look funny doing this exercise." In no time all
three were laughing so hard they had to let go of
the rings. They laughed and giggled all the way to
Station 5.

"A Tire Run!" exclaimed Estrell. "I've seen
football players do this exercise. It's good for
your legs."

"Here's an exercise that's good for your arm
muscles," said Stephanie at Station 6. "Let's
see how many of these Chin-Ups you can do, Estrell."

At Station 7 the children ran to a wall made of wood and chains. "Are we supposed to climb this?" asked Estrell.

"You bet," said Alfredo. "Come on, I'll race you both to the top."

The three of them reached the top together and agreed it was a tie. Slowly, they climbed down from the wall and moved on to Station 8.

"Body Curls," said Estrell as she read the sign. "Let's try these and then take a rest."

As the children rested, they discussed the trail. Estrell said her favorite exercises were the Jumping Jacks, the High Chair, Chin-Ups, and the Body Curls. Stephanie said she liked the Hip Circles best. Alfredo reminded them that they hadn't even finished the trail yet. There were still twelve more exercise stations.

"Twelve more!" moaned Estrell. "I think I will need to rest a lot longer!"

What Do You Think?

1. What is a physical fitness trail?
2. Which exercise station had an exercise that was good for the arm muscles?
3. Read the title of the bar graph below. What information will you find in the graph?
4. What do the numbers along the bottom of the graph tell you?
5. How many times did Estrell do chin-ups at exercise station 6?
6. Which exercise did Estrell do the most number of times?
7. Which exercises did Estrell do less than five times?

Estrell's Performance at Her Favorite Exercise Stations

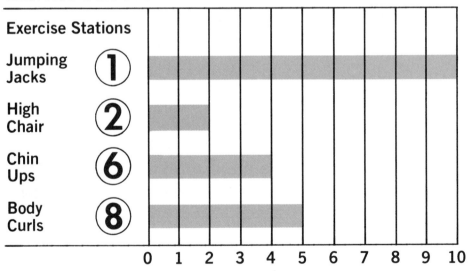

Number of times exercise was performed

Activity

Plan a fitness trail of your own. Include your favorite exercises.

TWO FABLES BY AESOP

retold by James Reeves

Wind and Sun

Wind and Sun had an argument one day about
who was stronger.

"I am stronger," boasted Wind, puffing out its
cheeks and blowing so hard that the leaves on the
trees shook. "You sit up there, Sun, and do
nothing but shine—that is, when I don't blow the
clouds across the sky. When that happens, you
can't even be seen! Of course, I'm stronger."

"Don't be too sure," answered Sun calmly, filling
the air with its warm radiance. "I'll tell you what.
We'll have a contest, shall we?"

"Certainly," said Wind. "Then everyone will know, once and for all, who is stronger. What shall the contest be?"

"See that person over there?" said Sun, gazing across the countryside toward a winding, white road. Along it walked a traveler with a cloak about his shoulders.

"I see him," said Wind.

"Well then, let's see which of us can get his cloak off first," said the Sun.

"That's easy. I'll have his cloak off his back in no time," said Wind.

So saying, Wind began to blow—*phoo–oo-oo*! The traveler on the road took no notice. But Wind had scarcely begun. Wind blew harder, and then harder still, till the water of the lakes turned to great waves, and the trees were bent almost double, and the birds in the air were dashed hither and thither with the force of the gale.

But the traveler, instead of taking his cloak off, only held it closer around him; and the harder Wind blew, the tighter the traveler clutched it. Even when Wind roared fearfully, and blew so hard as to snap the branches from the stoutest oaks, Wind could not get the traveler's cloak off his back.

At last Wind was tired out and could blow no more. It was Sun's turn. By now the sky was all covered over with dark storm clouds, but as soon as Wind stopped blowing they gently drifted apart, and Sun shone warmly down over the green fields.

Warmer and warmer grew the air under Sun's pleasant beams, and soon the traveler unbuttoned his cloak and let it hang loosely about him. Thanks to Sun's kindly heat the traveler was soon glad to take off the cloak altogether and carry it over his arm.

"There!" said Sun. "Which of us got the cloak off—tell me that."

Wind only growled and said nothing. But Wind knew Sun was stronger after all.

Gentleness can achieve more than violence.

Fox and Grapes

Reynard was hungry. For two whole days he had had nothing to eat. Not a rabbit had he caught in the fields; not a hen had he stolen from the farm. He began to think he would die of starvation.

That night, when everyone was in bed and the moon was peeping over the hill, he crept into a garden to have a look around. He sniffed curiously. All at once he noticed a most delicious smell. It was the smell of sweet, juicy grapes.

Reynard looked up. There they were, bunches and bunches of the big purple fruit, all ready to be picked.

Reynard licked his lips greedily and stretched himself upwards. But even when he stood on his hind legs so that he nearly fell over backwards, the grapes were still out of reach. So he crouched down almost to the ground and gave a mighty leap in the air. He couldn't even reach the lowest bunch.

Reynard looked around for another way to get at them. But it was useless. The vine grew against the wall of the house, and all the fruit was growing on the upper branches.

Once more Reynard took a few steps backwards and sprang at the grapes. Again and again he jumped, but not a single grape could he pull down. So when he was too tired to jump any more, he turned away and slunk out of the garden.

"Let the grapes rot!" he said angrily. "They're not worth bothering about. Anyone can see they're sour!"

People sometimes speak ill of what they can't get.

What Do You Think?
1. Why did Wind and Sun have a contest?
2. How did Sun win the contest?
3. Do you think Reynard really thought the grapes were sour? Why or why not?

Activities
1. Give an example to tell how being gentle might help you get something that you want.
2. Write a story that teaches a lesson. The lesson could be *You can't play all the time* or *Think twice before you do something.*

The Radio Code Mystery

by Thomas F. Pursell

"Hurry up, Bill," called Peg Adams to her brother as she ran down the front steps of their house. "Mr. Ernie wants us to come over."

Mr. Ernie was Ernie Mendez, the children's next-door neighbor. Now that he was retired, he spent a lot of time with his young friends.

When Bill and Peg hurried into Mr. Ernie's home, their friend smiled with pride and pointed toward something on a table.

"Wow!" exclaimed Bill. "A CB radio!"

Ever since Ernie Mendez had quit working, he had wanted to get a CB radio. Many people were buying these two-way radios for their cars and homes. They made up "call" names for themselves and often made new friends by talking over the radio.

Peg and Bill had all kinds of questions for Mr. Ernie about the radio.

"Hold on," laughed Mr. Ernie. "I'll tell you all about it. It's a Racer radio, and it has forty channels, or stations. I got this big radio, or base station, for the house and a smaller radio for the car. The only place in Lake City where they sell these CBs is at Marty's Hardware."

"What's going to be your call name?" asked Bill.

"Well, I think I'll call myself Mr. Ernie, just like you two do," replied their friend.

Mr. Ernie flipped on the switch, and the three sat and listened to the strange chatter.

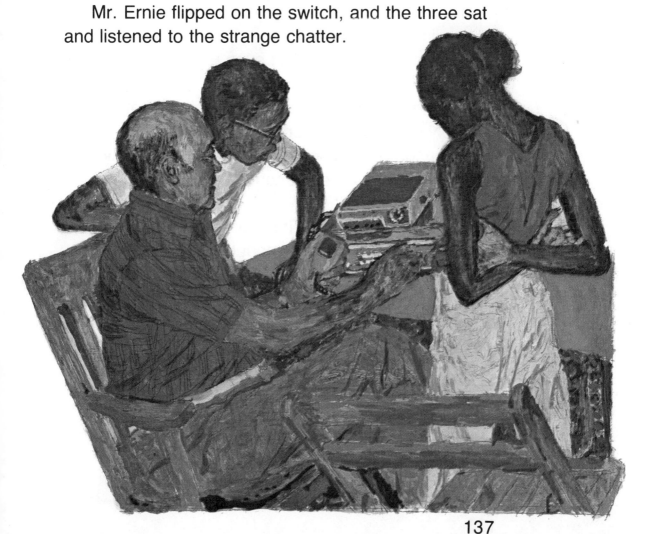

"CB people have a different way of saying things," Mr. Ernie explained. "For example, *come in* means 'I'm calling you.' Only one person talks at a time, so when somebody says 'over,' that means it's the other person's turn to talk. When you want to end a conversation, you say 'over and out.' "

Then a faint voice said over the CB, "Heavy Trucker, this is Mr. In. Come in, over." In a few seconds, another louder voice answered, "Mr. In, this is Heavy Trucker. Come in, good buddy."

"Heavy Trucker," repeated the first voice, "we're having Huntley Racers at eleven. Over and out." The radio went silent.

Peg complained, "I can't even understand what they're talking about."

"Don't feel bad, Peg," said Mr. Ernie. "That's probably some private code."

"It sounds pretty fishy to me," said Peg. "Why would Mr. In use a secret code unless he had something to hide?"

Mr. Ernie laughed. "That's probably just Mr. In's way of telling his friend to meet him for supper tonight."

The next morning, when Peg started reading the newspaper, she saw something that made her think about the mysterious radio code.

"Listen, Bill!" she said as she began to read from the newspaper. "'More than five thousand dollars' worth of goods were stolen last night from Al's Appliance Store in downtown Huntley. Police questioned the owner of the store, who said that the thieves took a whole shipment of Racer CB radios. Police report that there have been several similar robberies in recent weeks, all involving CB radios.'" Peg looked up from the newspaper. "Does that remind you of anything?" she asked.

"It sure does," said Bill seriously. "You might have been right about the mysterious radio message we heard yesterday afternoon. That could have been the thieves talking about Racer radios!"

Later that day when Peg and Bill came home from school, they told Mr. Ernie their idea about the radio code and the robbery in Huntley.

"Sounds pretty wild to me," said Mr. Ernie, stroking his chin. "But you just might be right. I'll tell you what—we'll listen to that channel again today. If we hear another message like that, and there's another robbery . . ."

"Mr. Ernie, look at the time!" cried Bill. "This is just the time we heard that message yesterday!"

As Mr. Ernie switched on the CB radio, they heard familiar voices. "Heavy Trucker, this is Mr. In. Come in, over."

"Heavy Trucker, we'll have Lake City Racers at ten. Over and out!"

"Lake City!" cried Peg. "That's our town. They must be going to rob Marty's Hardware tonight!"

"Not so fast, Peg," said Mr. Ernie. "That certainly does make sense, but we don't have any proof." Mr. Ernie looked thoughtful. "As long as this is Friday, ask your folks if you can stay up late tonight. Then at ten o'clock, we'll drive past Marty's and take a look."

Lake City was almost deserted when Mr. Ernie and the children drove through the business district.

"Everything looks OK from the front," said Mr. Ernie as they neared Marty's Hardware Store. "I'll drive by the alley, and we'll take a look down it."

Mr. Ernie slowed the car to a crawl as they passed the alley. Suddenly Peg yelled, "There they are!"

The three of them saw a huge truck without lights on pulling away from the back of the hardware store.

As Mr. Ernie stepped on the gas, he reached for the CB microphone to call the police.

"Wait a minute," said Peg. "I've got an idea . . ." Peg told him her plan, and Mr. Ernie began to talk on the CB.

The two men in the huge truck were surprised when their CB crackled to life, calling their code name. "Heavy Trucker, this is Mr. In. Come in, over."

Speaking into the microphone, the man answered the call. "Mr. In, this is Heavy Trucker. Go ahead, over."

"Heavy Trucker, there has been a change in plan . . . " The driver turned the truck around as the voice on the radio began giving instructions. Fifteen minutes later the driver turned into another dark alley.

"At last," said the driver. "Now we're supposed to pull up behind the fifth building on the right."

Suddenly the driver slammed on the brakes. "Let's get out of here!" yelled his partner.

But before they could move, a man in a blue uniform appeared out of nowhere. Then another popped up on the other side of the truck. The two men in the truck held up their hands as the whole alley began to swarm with police officers.

Peg and Bill, Mr. Ernie, and the police chief stepped out from a doorway. The alley was now full of light and noise as police officers took charge of the truck filled with stolen CB's.

"Thank you," said the chief, shaking hands with the three friends. "That was quite a plan you had, Peg, having Ernie direct those men all over Lake City and then here while you came over to warn us." The chief chuckled.

"Do you think you'll ever catch Mr. In, Chief?" asked Peg.

"Oh, sooner or later we will. But it won't be as easy as catching these two!" the police chief said, laughing. "Of course, it's not very hard to catch some thieves. Not when your friends have them drive right up to the back door of the police station!"

What Do You Think?

1. What was the problem in the story?
2. What was Peg's plan?
3. How did Peg's plan help solve the problem?
4. Which of these words would you use to describe Peg?

clever	neighborly	quick-witted
alert	complaining	friendly

5. What was the meaning of the mysterious radio code "We're having Huntley Racers at eleven"?

Activity

Make up a code using numbers for letters. Write a message in code to a friend.

The Tale of the Name of the Tree

a Bantu folktale retold by Pattie Price

There was at one time a great famine, or hunger, in the land. There grew in the land a great tree with fine fruit, but this fruit would only drop when someone spoke the name of the tree. So as the famine grew worse and worse, the people all came and lived near the tree, waiting for the fruit to ripen. When the fruit was almost ripe, it was discovered that no one knew the name of the tree!

So the people said, "Let us send Hare to Chief-over-the-Mountains so that the chief will tell us the name of the tree."

 From "The Tale of the Name of the Tree" from *Bantu Tales* by Pattie Price, 1938. Reprinted by permission of the author.

Hare then set forth and soon reached the kraal, or village, of Chief-over-the-Mountains. When she asked the chief for the name of the tree, the chief replied, "That tree is called U-wun-ge-lay-ma. When you get back, stand beneath it and say 'U-wun-ge-lay-ma,' and the fruit will fall."

So Hare hurried on her way back to the people. But she had not gone far on the path when she tripped over a root and rolled down the hill. And before she reached the bottom, the name of the tree had gone out of her head!

Hare tried all the names she knew and many others as she went along. She said, "Is it U-wun-tu-le-gay-le, or U-wayn-gay-le-tu-la, or what?" All the way she tried to remember, but when she arrived at the tree—although she tried many words—not a piece of fruit fell!

Now the people said they would send the antelope, or Springbok, to the chief. She was so swift she would return before she had forgotten the name. So Springbok set out and arrived there in no time. Then the chief told her, "That tree is called U-wun-ge-lay-ma."

Springbok started back as fast as she could to return to the people. But in her haste she tripped over an enormous ant hill, and before she could pick herself up the name was gone! She tried all the names she knew on the way, but in vain. When she got back, all she could say was, "U-wun-ge-lay-tum-ba," and *that* was no use!

So the people said they would send another antelope, Kudu, for he was stronger and would not fall on the way. Kudu set out and soon arrived at the chief's kraal. The chief told him, "The name of that tree is U-wun-ge-lay-ma." Kudu thanked the Chief-over-the-Mountains and started back.

But on his way Kudu caught his horns in the branches of a tree. While he was freeing himself, he forgot to say the name, and it went out of his head! When he had freed himself, the name was gone. And when he returned to the people, he had to admit that he had forgotten it.

The people now said they would send Lion, for
he was both swift and strong, and he had no
horns to catch in trees. Lion got the name from
Chief-over-the-Mountains and started home,
repeating the name to himself. But the sun was
hot, and he was tired. He lay down to rest in the
shade of a bush, and he slept. But when he woke,
he could not remember the name.

Now Lion was too proud to admit he had
forgotten the name, so he made up a name and
said it many times to the tree. But no fruit fell.

Then the people said, "Nonsense! There is no
such name! You are no better than the others, for
you have forgotten also."

And they were very sad, for their hunger was
growing and the fruit was ripening.

150

At last Elephant said, "Let us send Tortoise." All
the animals laughed for they were sure no one so
slow could remember.

But before Tortoise left, he went to his mother
and asked her, "How does one remember a very
hard word?"

His mother said, "If you wish to remember it, do
not stop saying it for any reason."

After a long time Tortoise reached the kraal of Chief-over-the-Mountains, and the chief told him, "That tree is called U-wun-ge-lay-ma." Tortoise asked him again, and the chief told him once again. Tortoise asked him a third time and the chief said the word yet again.

So then Tortoise set out, saying the name to himself. When he came to the ant hill, he said, "U-wun-ge-lay-ma," as he went around it. When he came to the tree, he just went on saying the word. And again when he came to the bush— although he was very tired and it was very hot— he only said, "U-wun-ge-lay-ma," and kept on.

At last he reached his home and his mother said, "You are very tired. Will you not rest?"

But the tortoise said, "U-wun-ge-lay-ma," and went on.

When he reached his friends underneath the tree, they all said, "What is the name? Tell us the name of the tree!"

Tortoise said, "U-wun-ge-lay-ma." And the fruit immediately began to fall.

The people ate and were hungry no longer. They said, "We will make Tortoise chief over all the people, for he has brought us the name of the tree!"

And now, can *you* remember what was the name of that tree?

What Do You Think?
1. Why did the people want the fruit from the tree?
2. Why couldn't anyone eat the fruit of the tree at the beginning of the story?
3. How was Tortoise able to remember the name of the tree?
4. Put the following sentences in the order in which they happen in the story.
   a. The Hare was sent to Chief-Over-the-Mountains.
   b. Tortoise asked his mother how one remembers a hard word.
   c. There was a great famine in the land.
   d. The fruit fell from the tree.
5. When you want to remember something, how do you do it?

Activity
Act out this story with your friends.

Two of Everything

by Alice Ritchie

Mr. and Mrs. Hak-Tak had always been rather poor. They had a small house in a village among the mountains and a tiny patch of green land on the mountainside. Here they grew the vegetables which were all they had to live on. When it was a good season and they did not need to eat everything as soon as it was grown, Mr. Hak-Tak took what they could spare in a basket to the next village. There he sold the vegetables for as much as he could get. Then he bought some oil for their lamp and fresh seeds to replant the patch.

Now one day when Mr. Hak-Tak was digging in his precious patch, he unearthed a big brass pot. He was disappointed to find that it was empty. Still, he thought, he and his wife would find some use for it. So when he was ready to go back to the house in the evening, he decided to take it with him. It was very big and heavy. In his struggles to get his arms round it, his money pouch fell to the ground. To be quite sure the pouch was safe, he put it inside the pot and so staggered home with his load.

As soon as Mr. Hak-Tak got into the house, Mrs. Hak-Tak hurried to meet him. "My dear husband, whatever have you got there?" she asked.

"I don't know," he replied. "I found it buried in our vegetable patch, and so far it has been useful in carrying our money home."

Mrs. Hak-Tak said, "Alas, something smaller would have done as well to hold any money we have now—or are likely to have." She stooped over the pot and looked into its dark inside.

As she stooped, her hairpin—for poor Mrs. Hak-Tak had only one hairpin—fell into the pot. She put in her hand to get it out again, and then she gave a loud cry.

"What is it?" Mr. Hak-Tak asked. "Is there a snake in the pot?"

"Oh, my dear husband," she cried. "What can be the meaning of this? I put my hand into the pot to fetch out my hairpin and your money pouch. And look, I have brought out two hairpins and two pouches, both exactly alike."

"Open both pouches," said Mr. Hak-Tak. "One of them will certainly be empty."

But it was not so. One pouch contained exactly the same number of coins as the other. It meant, of course, that the Hak-Taks had exactly twice as much money in the evening as they had had in the morning.

"And two hairpins instead of one!" cried Mrs. Hak-Tak. "There is something quite unusual about this pot."

"Let us put in the sack of lentils and see what happens," said Mr. Hak-Tak.

They heaved in the bag of lentils, which was so big it almost filled the pot. When they pulled the bag out again, they saw another bag of exactly the same size waiting to be pulled out. So now they had two bags of lentils instead of one.

"Put in the blanket," said Mr. Hak-Tak. "We need another blanket for the cold weather." And, sure enough, when the blanket came out, there lay another beneath it.

"Let us put in everything we have, in turn," said Mr. Hak-Tak. "What a pity we have no meat, for it seems that the pot cannot make anything without a pattern."

Then Mrs. Hak-Tak said, "My dear husband, let us put the pouch in again and again and again. If we take two pouches out each time we put one in, we shall have enough money by tomorrow evening to buy everything we lack."

"I am afraid we may lose it this time," said Mr. Hak-Tak. But in the end he agreed, and they dropped in the pouch and pulled out two. Then they added the new money to the old and replaced the pouch in the pot and pulled out the larger amount twice over.

After a while the floor was covered with leather pouches, and the Hak-Taks decided just to throw the money in by itself. It worked quite as well and saved trouble.

At last Mrs. Hak-Tak said, "My dear husband, there is no need for us to work so hard. We shall see to it that the pot does not run away, and we can always make more money when we want it. Let us tie up what we have."

The money made a huge bundle in the extra blanket, and the Hak-Taks looked at it for a long time before they slept. They talked of all the things they would buy and the improvements they would make in the cottage.

The next morning they rose early. Mr. Hak-Tak refilled a pouch with money and set off for the big village. He was going to buy more things in one morning than he had bought in a whole fifty years.

Mrs. Hak-Tak saw him off and then she tidied up the cottage and put the rice on to boil. Then she had another look at the bundle of money, and made herself a whole set of new hairpins from the pot. Next she made twenty candles instead of the one which was all they had possessed up to now. After that she slept for a while, having been up so late the night before.

But just before the time when her husband should be back, Mrs. Hak-Tak awoke and went over to the pot. She dropped in her cabbage leaf to make sure the pot was still working properly. She took two leaves out.

Then she knelt to look inside the brass pot, and at that moment her husband came to the door. Mrs. Hak-Tak turned quickly to see all the wonderful things he had bought, but she lost her balance and fell into the brass pot.

Mr. Hak-Tak put down his bundles and ran across and caught her by the ankles to pull her out. But no sooner had he set her carefully on the floor than he saw the kicking legs of another Mrs. Hak-Tak in the pot!

He could not leave her there, so he caught her ankles and pulled—another Mrs. Hak-Tak stood beside them! She was so exactly like the first that no one could have told one from the other.

"I will not have a second Mrs. Hak-Tak in the house!" screamed the first Mrs. Hak-Tak.

"One wife is all I want," wailed Mr. Hak-Tak.

"Put her back in the pot!" cried Mrs. Hak-Tak.

"What? And draw out two more?" said her husband. "If two wives are too many, so are three. No! No!" He stepped back quickly, and, missing his footing, he fell into the pot!

Both Mrs. Hak-Taks ran, and each caught an ankle and pulled him out and set him on the floor. But there was another pair of kicking legs in the pot! Again each caught hold of an ankle and pulled. Soon another Mr. Hak-Tak stood before them. He was so exactly like the first that no one could have told one from the other.

Now the first Mr. Hak-Tak liked the idea of his double no more than Mrs. Hak-Tak had liked the idea of hers.

But the first Mrs. Hak-Tak had a very good idea. "Listen, my dear husband," she said. "It is really a good thing that there is a new one of you as well as a new one of me. It means that you and I can go on in our usual way. These new people, who are ourselves and yet not ourselves, can set up house together next door to us."

And that is what they did. The first Hak-Taks built themselves a fine new house with money from the pot. They built one just like it next door for the new couple. They all lived together in the greatest friendliness.

The neighbors in the village were very much surprised at the sudden wealth of the Hak-Taks and at the new couple who resembled them so strongly. They thought the couple must be very close relations of the Hak-Taks.

The neighbors said, "It looks as though the Hak-Taks decided to have two of everything when they became rich. They even have two of themselves in order to enjoy their money more."

What Do You Think?

1. Could this story really have happened? Why or why not?
2. Put the following sentences in the order in which they happened in the story.
   a. Mrs. Hak-Tak pulled two pouches and two hairpins out of the pot.
   b. There were now two Mr. Hak-Taks.
   c. Mr. Hak-Tak fell into the brass pot.
   d. Mr. Hak-Tak dug up a brass pot.
3. Which of the following titles could be used for this story?
   a. The Money Pouch
   b. New Neighbors
   c. The Magic Brass Pot
4. Where did the new Hak-Taks live?

Activity

Write a story about what you would do if there were two of you.

THE MYSTERIOUS TADPOLE

by Steven Kellogg

Uncle McAllister lived in Scotland. Every year he sent Louis a birthday gift for his nature collection.

"This is the best one yet!" cried Louis when a live tadpole in a jar was delivered to the apartment door.

The next day Louis took the tadpole along with his entire collection of plants and rocks and shells to school for show-and-tell.

"This is a tadpole," said Louis, holding it up for the class to see. His teacher, Mrs. Shelbert, asked him to bring it back often so they could all watch it become a frog.

Louis named the tadpole Alphonse. Every day Alphonse ate several cheeseburgers. And every day he grew bigger and bigger.

Louis found that Alphonse was eager to learn. He became especially good at retrieving things.

When Alphonse became too big for his jar, Louis moved him to the sink. After Alphonse outgrew the sink, Louis's parents agreed to let him use the bathtub.

One day Mrs. Shelbert decided that Alphonse was not turning into an ordinary frog. She asked Louis to stop bringing him to school.

By the time summer vacation arrived, Alphonse was enormous.

"He's too big for the bathtub," said Louis's mother.

"He's too big for the apartment," said Louis's father.

"He needs a swimming pool," said Louis.

"There is no place in our apartment for a swimming pool," said his parents.

Louis suggested that they buy the parking lot next door and build a swimming pool. "It would cost more money than we have," said his parents. "Your tadpole will have to be donated to the zoo."

The thought of Alphonse in a cage made Louis very sad. Then, in the middle of the night, Louis remembered that the junior high had a swimming pool which nobody used during the summer.

Louis hid Alphonse under a rug and smuggled him into the school. After making sure that Alphonse felt at home, Louis went back to bed.

Every morning Louis spent several hours swimming with Alphonse. In the afternoon Louis earned the money for Alphonse's cheeseburgers by delivering newspapers.

Louis trained Alphonse to retrieve things from the bottom of the pool.

Summer vacation passed quickly. Louis worried what would happen to Alphonse now that school had reopened.

As soon as the first day ended, Louis ran to the junior high. The students were getting ready for after-school activities. Louis arrived just as the first swimming race began. Alphonse was delighted to see all the swimmers.

170

"It's a submarine from another planet!" bellowed the coach when he saw Alphonse. "Call the police! Call the navy!"

"No! It's a tadpole!" cried Louis. "He's my pet!"

The coach was upset and confused. "You have until tomorrow," he cried, "to get that creature out of the pool!"

Louis didn't know what to do. On the way home he met his friend Miss Seevers, the librarian, and he told her his problem.

Miss Seevers went back to the junior high school with Louis. But when she saw Alphonse, she was so shocked that she dropped her purse and the books she was carrying into the swimming pool. Alphonse retrieved them.

Then Miss Seevers telephoned Louis's Uncle McAllister in Scotland. He told her that he had caught the little tadpole in Loch Ness, a large lake near his cottage.

Miss Seevers told Louis, "I'm convinced your uncle has given you a very rare Loch Ness monster!"

"I don't care!" cried Louis. "He's my pet!" He begged Miss Seevers to help him raise enough money to buy the parking lot near his apartment so he could build a swimming pool for Alphonse.

Suddenly Miss Seevers had an idea. "In 1639 there was a battle in our city's harbor," she said. "A pirate treasure ship was sunk, and no one has ever been able to find it. But perhaps we can!"

The next morning Louis took Alphonse to the harbor. Miss Seevers and Louis rented a boat and rowed out into the harbor. In the middle of the harbor Louis showed Alphonse a picture of a treasure chest.

Alphonse disappeared under the water.

In no time at all Alphonse reappeared beside the boat. He held an old treasure chest that he had retrieved from the bottom of the harbor.

With the treasure in the chest Louis and Miss Seevers bought the parking lot and hired some helpers to build a swimming pool.

When the pool was completed, all the children in the city were invited to swim.

That night Louis said, "Alphonse, next week is my birthday, which means that we've been friends for almost a year."

Far away in Scotland Uncle McAllister was also thinking about the approaching birthday. While out hiking he discovered an unusual stone in a clump of grass and sticks.

"A perfect gift for my nephew!" he cried. "I'll deliver it in person!"

Uncle McAllister arrived at Louis's apartment and gave Louis the present. Louis couldn't wait to add it to his collection.

Suddenly a crack appeared in the stone. "Look at that!" cried Louis. "There's a bird inside—a big baby bird!" He thanked his uncle and told everyone, "*This* is the best gift yet!"

What Do You Think?

1. How did Louis get Alphonse?
2. Why did Mrs. Shelbert ask Louis to stop bringing Alphonse to school?
3. Where did Louis keep Alphonse during the summer?
4. What trick did Louis train Alphonse to do at the pool? How did it help in finding the treasure chest?
5. What things in the story could really have happened?

Activities

1. Make a list of animal tricks that you have seen or read about.
2. Make up a story about what happened to Louis and the bird.

A Hippo Yawned

by Arnold Spilka

A hippo yawned
And I looked inside
And saw three monkeys
Taking a ride.
Then one of them yawned
And I looked inside
And there were three bumble bees
Taking a ride.
Then one of them yawned
And I looked inside
And there were three little fleas
Taking a ride.
Then one of them yawned
And I looked inside
And there were three hippos
Taking a ride.

Fiona's Bee

by Beverly Keller

Fiona Foster went outside to fill her dog dish. Fiona did not have a dog, or any kind of pet. All she had was a dog dish. Every day, she put it on her porch and filled it with water. She was hoping some dog might drop by for a drink, stay a few minutes, and be her friend.

Fiona was hoping the dog's owner would come for the dog, stay an hour or so, and be her friend. That way, Fiona would get two friends out of filling one dog dish.

Adapted by permission of Coward, McCann & Geoghegan, Inc., and Blassingame, McCauley & Wood from FIONA'S BEE by Beverly Keller. Text copyright © 1975 by Beverly Keller.

So far, Fiona had no friends. "It's because you're too shy," her mother told her. "You have to go out and meet people."

"It's because you don't try," her father said. "You have to get out and greet people."

"I'll wait for someone to drop by," Fiona thought. "I'm not sure just how to treat people."

When Fiona went out to the porch, she saw that a bee had dropped in the dog dish! It was swimming around and around in the water.

Fiona knew no dog owner would want a pet to drink a bee. Even before she found new friends, she was in trouble with them.

The bee was in trouble too. It swam slower and slower. Then it gave up and went limp.

Fiona was kind to dumb animals, and smart ones, too, but she had heard the saying "mad as a wet hen." She was afraid to find out how mad a wet bee might be.

This poor thing was drowning, though. Very carefully, Fiona slid a twig under it. She planned to put the twig in a sunny spot, and run before she found out how mad a wet bee could be.

Instead, the bee dragged itself up the twig to her finger! Fiona did not move. She knew that anyone wearing a bee should stand still.

The bee was very small, and very wet, and very tired. It dragged itself up to Fiona's wrist. Fiona held her breath until her chest hurt.

"I cannot stand here for the rest of my life with a bee on me," she thought. Slowly, she put her arm on a sunny part of the porch railing. When the bee got warm and dry, she told herself, it would fly away.

The bee wiped its face with its front feet, like a kitten washing itself. It wiped its sides fast with its back feet. As it got dry, Fiona saw that it was fuzzy as a new kitten. She had never seen a bee face so close before. Bees have nice faces, she decided. Still, she would have been happier if this one had not been on her wrist.

After a time, the bee seemed to feel better. It crawled up to her shoulder. Then it settled down, as if the climb had made it tired. When Fiona looked down from the far corner of her right eye, she could see it. She was afraid to call for help. If anybody got that bee upset, it might sting the nearest thing. The nearest thing was Fiona.

"If I stand here any longer," she told herself, "I will faint. If I faint, this bee will be mad!"

She had an idea. She thought it was a brilliant idea. She would walk to the park and find a sunny spot full of flowers. When the bee saw flowers, it would fly off for a sip of nectar.

Very carefully, Fiona stepped off the first porch step. "Be calm, bee," she said. "This is for your own good." She moved as if she were carrying eggs on her head. In fifteen minutes, she had walked three blocks.

A girl pushing a baby stroller cried, "Don't move! You have a bee on you!"

"I know," Fiona said.

The girl's eyes got round as a dog dish. "You *know?*" she asked.

"I saved it from drowning," Fiona explained.

The girl peered at the bee. "Will it sting?"

"I don't know," Fiona said. "It didn't sting me."

182

The girl called to a boy on a bicycle, "Larry, look! A bee rides on this girl's shoulder because she saved its life!"

Larry stared at the bee. "Will it sting?"

Fiona was about to shrug, but she remembered the bee. "I think it likes me."

"What's your name?" the girl asked her.

"Fiona."

"I'm Barbara," the girl said. She pointed at the baby in the stroller. "That's my brother Roberto."

"I never met anybody who had a bee," Larry said. He walked his bike beside Fiona. "Aren't you afraid of things that sting?"

"If you know how to treat them, they're all right," Fiona said.

Two girls came running across the street. One yelled, "Look out! You have a bee on you!"

"It's her pet bee," Barbara said. "She saved its life."

The new girls followed Fiona, very carefully. They said they were Pauline and Martha.

At the park, Larry met his friends Bill and Howard, and Howard's dog Spike. "This girl wears a bee on her shoulder," he told them.

"It will sting anybody that bothers her," Pauline added.

"I need to find a place with flowers for my bee," Fiona told them.

Everybody helped her look. Finally, Spike found a sunny hill covered with clover.

"I'm going to sit down slowly, so my bee won't be upset," Fiona said. "When it remembers it's hungry, it'll fly to the clover for a snack."

"Will it come back to you?" Martha asked.

"I'm not going to wait," Fiona said. "Dogs and cats need people, but bees should be free."

Everybody waited for the bee to move. Barbara asked where Fiona lived. Martha invited Fiona to play Ping-Pong at her house. Pauline asked Fiona to come to the movies Saturday. Larry told Fiona she could ride his bike. Bill said she could feed his turtle sometime. Howard gave her half a glass marble. Spike shook her hand.

The bee moved its wings. Everybody but Fiona stood back. Barbara held Roberto. Howard picked up Spike. The bee flew—swoop—right to a clover!

After everyone bid the bee good-by, they walked home with Fiona. Sitting on her porch, they talked about training bees and seals and cobras. Roberto sat in the dog dish.

When it was time to go, everybody but Spike and Roberto said, "See you tomorrow," to Fiona. Spike shook her hand. Roberto waved to the dog dish.

"Did you have a good day?" Fiona's father asked her at supper.

"Did you find any friends?" her mother asked.

"I saved a bee, and I got famous," Fiona said. "I don't know if I'll still be famous tomorrow, but I sure have a lot of new friends."

What Do You Think?

1. What was Fiona's problem at the beginning of the story?
2. Why did Fiona put her dog dish on the porch? Do you think Fiona's idea was a good one?
3. What did Fiona find in her dog dish?
4. What did Fiona decide to do when the bee crawled on her? Do you think her idea was a good one?
5. How did the bee help Fiona with her problem?
6. How do you think Fiona felt when the bee flew away? Why do you think that?
7. After the bee flew away, what did Fiona's new friends do that showed they liked Fiona?
8. Do you think the way Fiona's problem of making friends was solved was a good one? Why or why not?
9. What does the saying "mad as a wet hen" mean?
10. In the sentence below, what does the underlined part mean?
    The girl's eyes <u>got round as a dog dish</u>.

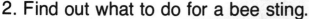

Activities

1. Read some books to learn more about bees.
2. Find out what to do for a bee sting.

The Way to Start a Day

by Byrd Baylor

The way to start a day
is this—

Go outside
and face the east
and greet the sun
with some kind of
song
that you made yourself
and keep for
early morning.

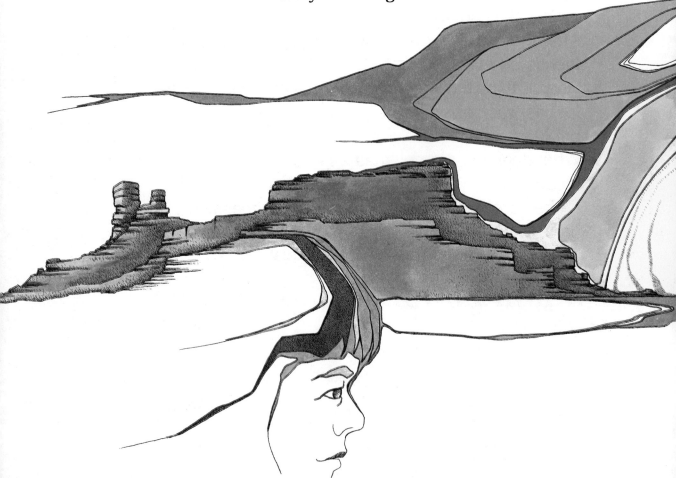

The way to make the song
is this—

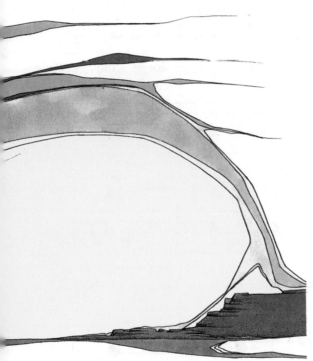

Don't try to think
what words to use
until
you're standing there
alone.

When you feel the sun
you'll feel
the song too.

Just sing it.

If the sky turns a color
sky never was before

just watch it.

That's part of the magic.
That's the way
to start
a day.

THIS LAND IS YOUR LAND

by Woody Guthrie

Chorus: This land is your land, — This land is my land, — From Cal – i – for – nia — to the New York is – land; — From the red-wood for – est — to the Gulf Stream wa – ters; — This land was made for you and me. —

Verses:

1. As I went walking that ribbon of highway,
   I saw above me that endless skyway,
   I saw below me that golden valley,
   This land was made for you and me.

2. I roamed and rambled, and I followed
       my footsteps,
   To the sparkling sands of her diamond
       deserts,
   All around me a voice was sounding,
   This land was made for you and me.

3. When the sun came shining, then I was
       strolling,
   And the wheat fields waving, and the
       dust clouds rolling,
   A voice was chanting as the fog was lifting,
   This land was made for you and me.

191

CLOUDS

by Christina Georgina Rossetti

White sheep, white sheep,
On a blue hill,
When the wind stops
You all stand still.
When the wind blows
You walk away slow.
White sheep, white sheep,
Where do you go?

"Clouds" by Christina Georgina Rossetti
Poems for the Children's Hour.
The Platt & Munk Co., Inc. 1927.